MILLINGTON'S MISSION

MILLINGTON'S MISSION

John Samuels

HarperCollins*Publishers*

HarperCollins*Publishers*

First published in Australia in 2002
by HarperCollins*Publishers* Pty Limited
ABN 36 009 913 517
A member of the HarperCollins*Publishers* (Australia) Pty Limited Group
www.harpercollins.com.au

HarperCollins*Publishers*
25 Ryde Road, Pymble, Sydney NSW 2073, Australia
31 View Road, Glenfield, Auckland 10, New Zealand
77–85 Fulham Palace Road, London W6 8JB, United Kingdom
Hazelton Lanes, 55 Avenue Road, Suite 2900, Toronto, Ontario, M5R 3L2
and 1995 Markham Road, Scarborough, Ontario, M1B 5M8, Canada
10 East 53rd Street, New York NY 10022, USA

National Library of Australia Cataloguing-in-publication data:

Samuels, John.
    Millington's mission.
    ISBN 0 7322 6922 9.
    1. Millington, Tasman, 1896–1964. 2. World War, 1914–1918 –
    Campaigns – Turkey – Gallipoli Peninsula. 3. Soldiers –
    Australia – Biography. 4. War memorials – Turkey –
    Gallipoli Peninsula. 5. World War, 1939–1945 – Secret
    service – Great Britain. 6. Spies – Australia – Biography.
    I. Title.
940.426

Cover design by Luke Causby, HarperCollins Design Studio
Typeset in 12.5/18.5 Bembo by HarperCollins Design Studio
Printed and bound in Australia by Griffin Press on 79gsm Bulky Paperback White

5 4 3 2 1   02 03 04 05

FOR ESMERELDA

eheu! fugaces labuntur anni ad infinitum,

fide et amore, finis coronat opus.

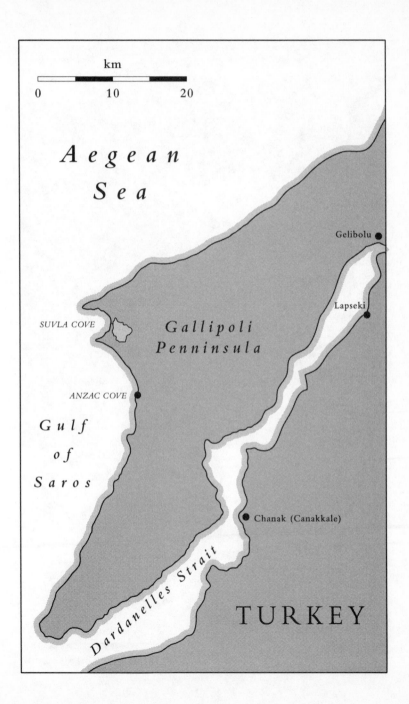

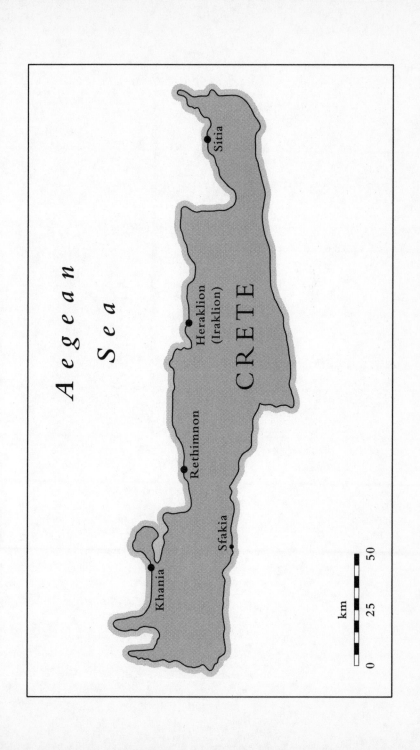

ONE

The last time Tasman Millington was there the sounds of war had hammered them without pause, but now an infinite silence extended in every direction. The trenches were empty too: he remembered the faces of the living pressed down on broken bodies of the dead. Smoke from a thousand campfires, their billies on the boil, had hung like limpid fog. The smoke was long gone and the Diggers who'd lit the fires had gone with it; only a rusting billy or two remained. And Johnny Turk had been in his trenches just over there, close enough for you to hear him cough, for you to share the smell of his rotting mates; certainly close enough to kill him when he poked his head over the parapet.

Tasman picked up a shin bone, brittle and dry, bleached white from the sun's rays of long summers – a single human bone in a vast sea of unknown remains that were once the living youth of a nation. It may even have come, Tasman realised, from someone he'd known. Wild grasses grew now over the shell-torn earth, as if to hide or perhaps protect its mournful secrets. A breeze made the taller blades sing in a solemn lament as Tasman walked to the edge of a slit trench. It wasn't as deep as he'd remembered but it was deep enough to make you scramble down the side if you wanted to reach the bottom. Wind and rain were gradually covering up the scars that men had made; rusted barbed wire and pieces of discarded equipment were the only sign of former human occupation. Further along the trench lay the remains of dugouts long abandoned by the men who had sweated and frozen there, cooking their tucker and sleeping in the mud; men who had lived their lives by the minute and bled and died there.

Four years and a lifetime ago Tasman had gone ashore at Gallipoli with the 26th Battalion, a fresh-faced young Digger from Hobart who'd joined up for the great adventure in the service of the Empire. That great adventure soon turned into a horror that no young bricklayer from Tasmania could ever have imagined. The fight with Johnny Turk was well entrenched by the time the 26th Battalion arrived in August 1915, and the fighting had become largely a matter of sniper versus sniper rather than the frantic charges between trenches of a few months before. Nonetheless, Gallipoli was still a deadly place and the men on both sides knew only too well that an exposed head could bring a sudden rifle crack and instant death. And another enemy was always waiting to strike – dysentery, which spread through the troops like wildfire.

It was this crippling condition that led to the young Private Millington being removed to an Aid Station and transferred to the Greek island of Mudros, where his health grew worse until he was taken on board a hospital ship for further treatment in Malta. Tasman's dysentery was so life-threatening that in late November medical officers sent him to England, after which he was admitted to the Birmingham War Hospital. It wasn't until mid-April that he was able to rejoin his unit in France. The 26th Battalion had moved to France in March 1916 from Egypt. It was involved in duties around Armentières, then engaged the Germans in a bloody battle for the Pozières Heights on 27 July. Tasman was wounded in the action, a bullet getting too close to his ear. Again he was admitted to hospital for treatment but, gunshot wound or not, he returned to his unit, which carried on the business of war throughout the Somme until November.

Tasman must have thought that the war was going to kill him one way or another, because early in December he was struck down again with dysentery, which put him out of action until June 1917. He rejoined his unit and fought with the battalion at Menin Road, Broodseinde and Passchendaele in October. The war rolled on for him – just as it has for a million others before and since – until the Battle of Amiens in August, where he was once more wounded in action. The gunshot ripped into his right forearm and tore away a tattoo. For years afterwards he joked that it was the greatest loss of the whole war. Tasman was sent to the war hospital in Bath and while he was there a chance meeting with a young Intelligence officer changed his life.

Tasman Millington was, as far as British Intelligence were concerned, the perfect man for a dual role they had in mind. He was from Australia, he was a tradesman, and he was now an ordinary soldier who'd seen war at the sharp end and had twice been hit by enemy gunfire. But best of all they saw in him a young man who could fit into any situation and quietly get the job done in a world that would be very different when the war was over. Tasman was sent to the British School of Telegraphy in London to be trained in the use of radio.

The Great War eventually passed into the history books and almost immediately the Allies set up the Imperial War Graves Commission to take responsibility for the proper burial of tens of thousands of fallen soldiers – men lying in hastily dug communal graves or left to decay where they fell. The dreadful task required men who were not only devoted to their duty but also had a strong stomach. Hearing about the War Graves Commission, Tasman decided, at the urging of British Intelligence, to put his name forward. He was demobilised in London in November 1919 and sent back to the Dardanelles, where only four years earlier he'd arrived amid all the horrors that followed the bungled landings there.

TWO

The War Graves Commission gave Tasman the use of an old house at Chanak, across the narrows from the Gallipoli Peninsula. It would be his home for many years. When required, Millington would take a motor launch, together with equipment and local workers, to the former battlegrounds at Gallipoli. Turkey had made the whole Peninsula a military area, which didn't make the Commission's work any easier. On leaving his house, Tasman – despite holding a position of authority – was escorted by a Turkish soldier at all times, and the early days of two old enemies living with each other were tense to say the least. But Tasman had a further problem: it was impossible for him at first to use the contents of a large timber packing case that had been sent from London. The crate held the components of a powerful radio transmitter. British Intelligence wanted regular reports from him that would give advance warning of any renewed military buildup in the region and perhaps help maintain the postwar peace with Turkey. Tasman could only assemble the radio and then hide it and wait until the time was right to install it somewhere; but under the watchful eyes of the Turkish Army that could be months away.

On his first crossing to Gallipoli, where the war dead awaited identification and burial, the madness and horror struck him once more. There in the silence, on the shell-shattered earth, lay the bones of unburied soldiers – in some places a few, in other places scores of them piled up like a scene from a slaughterhouse. The men lay where they'd fallen. The War Graves Commission had already decided that, given the huge area involved, the remains of the war dead would have to be buried at each place they were found. This of course meant that the Commission would have to create not one lone cemetery but dozens of them, all over the Peninsula. Here and there, too, the rain, wind and packs of wolves had scattered the bones far and wide, which told Tasman that identification of the dead would for the most part be hopeless. Then there were the mass graves that had been dug to prevent the rapid spread of disease through the trenches. Some of them might hold scores of bodies, but at least there was a chance of finding out who the men were.

The Turkish workers were bemused at the actions of the Commission's 'Foreign Devils' who were so concerned with the dead. The Turks had simply dug huge holes and disposed of their own war casualties – some 87 000 of them – in unmarked mass graves. Now, though, the digging teams were halted every time they unearthed remains, and markers were put in place until a supervisor could try to make some sort of identification of the body or bodies. Emotions ran deep among the Commission staff, not least Tasman who treated every disinterment with the dignity and respect usually afforded a close family member. He insisted that the Turkish workers remove their headgear and never touch a soldier's bone once it was exposed. This insistence caused the Turks to walk off the job on many occasions in the early days, but Tasman would just return to Chanak and hire more men – who would also quit when emotion poured out of him. Frustrated by all of this, the Commission's Inspecting Caretaker appointed a go-between whose job was to make Tasman's orders and requirements clear to the Turkish workers.

The man chosen was himself an ex-soldier. Pasha Ismail, a veteran of the trenches at Gallipoli, was an educated fellow who spoke English well. Ismail was somewhat shocked by his first meeting with Tasman Millington. From the stories he'd heard he expected the young man to be three metres tall with an attitude to match his reputation as a hard Australian veteran with no love whatever for his former enemy. Instead Ismail found himself aboard the launch one morning with a man barely 173 centimetres in height and of slim build, who constantly rolled cigarettes that were very thin at one end and finger-thick at the other.

On that morning Tasman said nothing to Ismail; as a result Ismail said nothing to him. The digging progressed all day and late in the afternoon Tasman and the other staff went with the workers to the encampment where they'd lived for well over a year. The routine was simple at the camp: the Turks would sit on one side and the Commission men on the other, few words being spoken as they all had their evening meal. Tasman was surprised when Ismail walked over to him and asked if they might talk about the next day's work. Tea was poured from the blackened billy and, much to Ismail's amazement, Tasman turned out to be a more than reasonable man, even offering the Turk one of his funnel-like cigarettes, from which most of the tobacco fell out the moment they were lit.

After that, things improved all round. The workers showed respect for the remains of the dead, and Tasman noted that more than once the Turks bowed their heads during the reburials and even went as far as standing at attention during the brief service conducted for each dead soldier. Ismail was a good, reliable man and before long they were all working as a team.

The passing months turned into years until, in 1925, Tasman was appointed Caretaker. Over the years he'd assumed that the people back in London had forgotten they'd sent him to radio school for a reason. The timber crate holding the transmitter parts had gathered a lot of dust when a letter arrived from the British diplomatic mission in Istanbul. It contained a signal from the British Admiralty, saying that Tasman Millington was to waste no time in setting up a listening station so that radio traffic between the military powers in that part of the world could be monitored more closely. 'After all,' the signal went on, 'remember the Trojan Horse.'

The Turkish Army generally still escorted Tasman wherever he went from his house in Chanak, but over time a moderate trust had built up which allowed him to wander off now and then on his own. However, setting up a radio post right under the noses of the Turks wasn't going to be easy, and if he was caught the result could well be an end to building a lasting memorial to the Anzacs, or even the end of Tasman himself. His work on the Peninsula gave him the opportunity to scout for suitable hidden locations for a radio aerial, but the barren landscape offered nothing suitable.

More months passed and then he received another signal from the Admiralty. Again it contained the same words: 'Remember the Trojan Horse.' Tasman thought it an unusual phrase, probably used by some pretentious young officer showing off his history education to the 'colonial boy' out in the Dardanelles. It would have been far better if the smart young bastard had sent him an invisible aerial and an equally invisible tree to hang it on. Trojan Horses and radio transmitters didn't really have much to do with each other, even though the ancient ruins of Troy lay not far from Chanak ...

Suddenly Tasman caught on.

THREE

With the exception of a few locals tending their flocks, the ruins at Troy were pretty much deserted and a perfect place to conceal Tasman's transmitter. The problem was going to be keeping everyone in the dark about his activities – the Turkish soldiers and the employees of the War Graves Commission. Whatever he decided to do, Tasman knew he'd have to work without their help.

Pasha Ismail owned an old truck that he'd salvaged from the war. It wasn't much to look at but it spluttered and rattled its way along the goat tracks the locals called roads and didn't let Ismail down too often. Tasman thought he could probably use the Turk's truck to move the transmitter from Chanak to

Troy. The next hurdle would be getting the crate through without anyone discovering its contents. At this point he had a very clever idea.

Over the years the Gallipoli Peninsula had yielded up far more than the war dead. Almost every day the Turkish workers exposed unexploded shells and unused explosives, highly unstable munitions. The explosives were always removed to a central point and covered with a tarpaulin until they could be detonated safely. Bombs and shells were usually put into large timber boxes lined with sand at the bottom to cradle the ordnance while it was carried away by Turkish soldiers. For obvious reasons the boxes were always treated with great care, and no rational man wanted to open them again and take a close look at the rusting and weeping bomb or shell inside.

The work went on its quiet, ritualistic way: graveyards to be made, graves to be dug, graves to be filled with yet another sad shroud. It seemed to Tasman that the Gallipoli Peninsula was like the stage for a tragic play – the curtain now rung down but the actors all lying dead, deaf to the thunderous applause of their grateful countrymen. The Turkish craftsmen, who worked the stone as their forebears had always done, put in long hours every day to supply headstones for the gravesites, which grew steadily in number. Tasman considered his first duty to be to the fallen Anzacs and that anything else must take second place. Nonetheless, the problem of the transmitter had to be taken care of.

During the digging one morning two workers unearthed a small cache of rusty shells as they'd done a thousand times before, but this time Tasman seized the moment and told the army guard that among the ordnance was a very dangerous 'quake bomb' that had been constructed by Australian soldiers. The quake bomb, Tasman told the guard, would explode like a volcanic eruption if anyone so much as breathed on it. The frightened Turkish soldier bought the story. Tasman volunteered his Australian expertise in dealing with the potential death trap, suggesting that everyone should be cleared from the area while he alone loaded it into a bomb box. There was no argument from the guard or the Turkish workers about that, and having brought the crate to Tasman they all scurried away without looking back. Tasman then took his time putting the big shell to bed in the sand-bottomed box. He had carefully chosen a harmless dead shell so that he wouldn't blow himself up while he carried out his little deception. When the guard finally walked back toward the crate it was to hear that Tasman could not defuse the dreaded Australian device without special tools that he had at home.

There was only one solution, Tasman said. The quake bomb would have to be loaded aboard the launch and taken across to the boathouse at Chanak, where he would make it safe. The guard now wanted to know why the bomb could not just be exploded where it was. Tasman explained that the bomb was designed by Australian engineers during the war to actually trigger an earthquake; he added that he'd be happy to detonate it with a mile-long fuse if the guard wanted to take responsibility for the quake that would follow. The man shook his head and said that he'd leave it to Tasman. The long walk through the hills had never been taken with such careful steps as Tasman and the soldier carried the crate between two poles, the Turk in front with a fearful look on his face and Tasman behind with a smirking grin on his. The trek took all afternoon and when they reached the motor launch it was almost nightfall. The quake bomb was loaded aboard and lashed down securely, then Tasman took the *Mary* out into the night, with the guard perched as far back in its stern as he could get.

Just before sunrise they sighted the boathouse and, once there, the guard quickly went ashore, rejoining Tasman just long enough to escort him to his house, where the 'special tools' were kept. Tasman made a show of calling for two other soldiers to help him carry the 'tool chest' down to the boat. The two men placed the box on the deck and then moved a considerable distance away from the boathouse while Tasman went to work on the bomb.

He now called on skills he hadn't had to use in years – skills he'd learnt in the Australian Army that enable you to look as though you're doing something when in fact you're doing nothing. And that is mostly what Tasman was doing, not that the Turkish soldiers would have guessed it as he tapped away at the brass case of the dud bomb, pausing only for a few moments as he seemed to straighten up to relieve his aching back. Finally he called the men over and gave them more bad news: the quake bomb, left to the elements all these years, was unable to be made safe and was an even greater threat after all that work on it.

Tasman briefed the two men on the huge disaster that would occur should the quake bomb go off and, rolling one of his conical cigarettes, said that the only thing he could think of was to take it far away from Chanak – somewhere he could encase it in stones and perhaps check up on it once a week or so to make sure it was undisturbed. But where? The senior guard was very helpful and suggested the ancient ruins at Troy, which lay south of Chanak. The ruins were deserted and safe. Tasman should go there, now, and take the quake bomb with him.

Tasman said he'd think about it. First he had to contact Pasha Ismail and persuade him to make his truck available. Leaving the two soldiers to guard the boat and its cargo, he went in search of the Turk. The first question Ismail asked was whether he'd be compensated if the bomb blew up. Tasman just smiled and said that if it did neither of them would have to worry about it. A very concerned Ismail reluctantly agreed to drive him to Troy.

Tasman had not had a sore back when he stopped work on the bomb for a moment or two – he had used the pause to quietly slip the bomb over the side of the launch and replace it with the transmitter from the 'tool chest'. With Ismail's help he secured the crate on the back of the truck and, unescorted by guards, the two men set out for Troy.

The road had potholes bigger than some of the shell craters on the other side of the narrows, and Ismail had to drive with extreme caution. But the road, the grades and the condition of the old truck all played their part in the inevitable: finally the wheels ground to a stop, with the radiator hissing steam from its tired coils. The pair were halfway to Troy and in the middle of nowhere. Night fell quickly and the mercury was falling fast by the time Tasman and Ismail had set up camp and built a fire. The truck would no doubt be fine in the morning and at least the 'bomb' wasn't being bounced around on the tray. Chicken and cheese with a little local wine soon relaxed the men.

Tasman and Ismail had been on friendly terms ever since they'd shared a cigarette that night in the Commission's encampment at Gallipoli, but this night felt different. Here were two ex-soldiers, who not all that long ago would have shot at each other without a thought, sitting down and sharing goat cheese and wine as if the war had never happened. Ismail gazed into the cloud-cloaked night and poured more wine into Tasman's tin mug. 'What's in the box, Millington?' he asked.

The answer came without hesitation. 'It's a radio transmitter – a big bugger. I understand the newer ones are a lot smaller.'

Ismail shot to his feet, waving his arms about and screaming a remarkable range of obscenities in English and Turkish. His comments then turned to the mad Australian who would surely get them both shot by the authorities and leave Ismail's wife a widow and his three beautiful children fatherless and penniless and certain in the knowledge that his poor pathetic body had been dumped on a garbage tip after being tortured all over, and the fact that the thing on his truck wasn't a bomb that caused earthquakes at all, it was a lie made up by a mad Australian, meant he must return to Chanak in the morning and report it to the authorities and explain to them that through no fault of his own he had been working with Millington and the Commission and one day had inadvertently gone to the boathouse and picked up a wooden box containing a radio transmitter and driven it without escort toward Troy – Ismail gasped for breath – and then maybe all would be forgiven!

Silence returned to the camp. Ismail sat and stared into the flickering flames as Tasman rolled another of his awful cigarettes, not having said a word. Eventually Tasman, who'd had plenty of time to think about what he was going to say, cleared his throat and quietly told Ismail that due to certain small problems now in the past, such as the war and then the 'Chanak crisis' of 1922 and 1923 when once again Britain and Turkey were on the brink of war, the British felt it was in the interests of both countries to keep watch on those who could disturb their alliance now that Turkey was a republic. He added that Ismail would be doing his nation a great deed if he helped set up the wireless station.

Ismail reflected for some time before asking if Tasman knew what the end result would be if they were found out. Tasman responded by saying that the only way the authorities were going to know was if Ismail made the mistake of telling the Turkish Army or anyone else. After another long silence Ismail said that, should they be caught, Tasman alone must take the blame. The Australian gave his word that he'd keep Ismail in the clear regardless of what happened. While Ismail wasn't entirely convinced, he agreed to go along with the scheme.

Early the next morning they set out again for Troy, the old truck's radiator topped up with water. Their conversation now was more like that of two men who'd known one another for years but never looked closely enough to see the real man inside. As Ismail's truck crawled its way along the road the talk turned to family matters and how they had things in common, separated by little more than birth and fate. Ismail spoke of his wife and his evil mother-in-law who lived with them and was in the finest of health, which could only suggest to him that she would remain a plague on his house for many more years to come. He also told Millington about his two daughters and son, who were clearly a bright light in his life.

Tasman too had much to say about his own beloved wife at home in Chanak and their young son, Bernard, who'd been born in Istanbul and christened on Anzac Beach, on Anzac Day 1922. Ismail listened with great interest as Millington talked of his wife's skill and passion for painting watercolours and their plans to send Bernard to a good boarding school in England when he was old enough. Tasman also spoke of his great love of boats and his broad experience in seamanship gained in the often wild waters of Tasmania.

Tasman conceded that Tasmania was far enough away from Turkish soil to call it the end of the earth; Ismail pointed out that as it was the same distance, perhaps it was Turkey that was the end of the earth. Both men laughed. Ismail had been brought up and educated in England before the family returned home and he'd been, like Tasman, drawn to soldiering.

Finally they reached Troy. The site rises steeply above the Trojan plain that separates it from the sea and it had kept its secrets until excavations by the German archaeologist Heinrich Schliemann exposed some of its stonework to the light again. Tasman hoped it could hold one last secret, the transmitter. He found in one of the crumbling walls a cavity that was a perfect place to hide the radio. The ground aerial thoughtfully provided by London wasn't the best but, given the topography of the wide Trojan plain, reception was good on the outdated set.

They headed back to Chanak, where Tasman was summoned before a Turkish colonel at army headquarters in the fortress of Cimenlik. The colonel came straight to the point. The quake bomb – was it now safe and well away from Chanak? Tasman had been expecting a long interrogation, but instead the officer offered him coffee and thanked him for risking his life to save Turkish citizens. The colonel added that the army had never wanted to kill Australians during the bad days of war; they liked Australian soldiers and much admired them for the sense of fair play and decency they showed the Turkish troops.

Tasman told the colonel that the quake bomb was safe for the moment, but it would be necessary for him, Tasman, to check it every few days, just to make sure.

Much to Ismail's relief when Tasman saw him a little later, the colonel had approved the idea and had said that the two men would be given travel passes and fuel vouchers for their trips to Troy. This arrangement, as it turned out, was to continue for many years, despite the changing parade of senior Turkish officers who in time knew nothing of its origins.

FOUR

The cemeteries on the Peninsula now numbered 31, commemorating some 49000 men. But many, many more war dead would be located in the months and years to come. Not a day went by when the long steel rod driven into unworked ground failed to find the grey-green sludge of another decomposed corpse. Uncovered, the body could sometimes be identified; often it could be known only as a soldier of the Great War. Some remains had to be left in place.

Pilgrimages to Gallipoli had begun on a small scale in 1925 after the official dedication of the memorials, but in the following year the *Stella d'Italia* arrived with a complement of 300 passengers. They were landed one September afternoon at Kilye Bay, where they were met by officers of the Imperial War Graves Commission, Tasman among them. The passengers, some of whom were veterans of Gallipoli, included wives or mothers of those who'd not returned – women seeking to close a chapter of their lives by finding the grave of a loved one, or at least feeling as if they'd been near their husband or son.

Also among the passengers was someone Tasman hadn't seen in a long time. The uniform was gone, but there was no mistaking the British Intelligence officer who'd been responsible for Tasman going to radio school in England. The two men greeted each other warmly and sat down to talk. It wasn't long until the true reason for the Englishman's visit was revealed. London wanted far more regular reports from Tasman and of a much broader scope – including details of the movements of all large vessels using the Dardanelles and anything he could discover as to the nature of their cargoes. Tasman was taken aback by the request, which to him seemed more like an order. He was running the transmitter operation at Troy, spending what time he could listening to military frequencies, hearing nothing of any great consequence and reporting the same to London. In all the time he'd been doing this second job he'd never once considered himself to be some sort of spy, but apparently that was just what British

Intelligence wanted him to be. Reluctantly, yet feeling that he had little choice, Tasman agreed.

He did have one thing in his favour, he realised. Over the years he had developed considerable skill in seamanship, and not only in the crowded waters of the Dardanelles. In 1922, when the Turks took Smyrna (now Izmir) from the Greeks, Tasman had used one of the Commission's vessels to help evacuate Greek soldiers from the burning city's quayside – no mean feat. On other occasions he'd spent time poking around the islands of the northeast Aegean.

In 1928 Tasman was made Inspecting Caretaker and, only six months later, Superintendent of Gallipoli. With his promotion came a better house in Chanak. His duty to the Anzac legends was still the first priority for him. His trips across the narrows with Ismail to check on the work of the gardeners and stonemasons were just as moving as the first trip had been in 1919. And where once there was nothing but death, now new life grew from the bloodied soil in the form of cypress pines and Judas shrubs planted at every war cemetery. The air, once filled with the stench of decay, now carried the scent of rosemary.

In December 1936, five months after a revision of the Treaty of Lausanne allowed Turkey to refortify the Dardanelles and the Bosporus, which runs from the Sea of Marmara to the Black Sea, Tasman was asked to undertake a mission which nearly ended in disaster. Certain Intelligence officers in London wanted him to take what they called a sightseeing trip up through the Dardanelles into the Sea of Marmara, and they thought it would be an 'outstanding favour' if he could 'see his way clear' to take a camera and record anything of interest.

Ismail shook his head in disbelief when Tasman told him what he'd been asked to do, and for the very first time Tasman made it clear that he didn't want Ismail to come with him, as he fully expected things to go wrong. So it was a surprised Tasman who found Ismail at his door the next day with a bag containing a camera and film. Ismail told Tasman that he'd be mad to go alone and that, after all, few people could understand his Australian version of the Turkish language at the best of times.

They decided to take the motor launch, the *Mary*, for the round journey of some 200 kilometres. After refuelling at Lapseki, Ismail's home town, where his wife gave them dinner and they spent the night, they headed up to the Marmara past fleets of local fishing boats working close inshore. Freighters made their way up and down the centre of the strait, but they were ordinary cargo ships with ordinary cargoes and Tasman could see nothing that he should be photographing.

It was the same when they reached the Sea of Marmara. There was no shipping there that would tease the suspicions of Tasman's London masters. But there was something that concerned Tasman. As Marmara Island loomed up in the distance, ominous clouds ahead indicated an approaching violent storm. Shortly after nightfall the tempest enveloped the launch, the sea turning into a rolling field of flying whitecaps.

The *Mary* rolled and pitched and raced down the side of deep troughs, then climbed its way to the cresting wavetops where the gale-force wind slashed the spray about as though it were being wielded by a swordsman. Tasman fought the wheel to keep the bow to the wind, but the course toward Marmara Island grew more erratic by the minute. Through the howl of the wind Ismail shouted to Tasman that he thought he'd glimpsed a light over on the port side. As the *Mary* rose from another deep trough Tasman saw a flash of light himself, but there was no way of knowing whether it was on the shore or was a ship's lamp. Ismail now discovered that the *Mary* was taking water and went below. He was thrown violently around the cabin but, bracing himself on his knees, he began bucketing the seawater up through the companionway. If he was going to die, he thought, at least he'd be on his knees before God.

Still fighting the wheel, Tasman decided to steer in the direction of the light they'd seen. As he turned the *Mary* to port the motor slowed and the steering became useless. Tasman pulled up the hatch cover above the engine compartment and was showered with a blast of oily water thrown up by the flywheel, which was half submerged in the flooded bilge. He shouted to Ismail to come and help. As the Turk clambered up the steps he was suddenly flung back down the companionway as a loud cracking sound rang out, followed by a grating and grinding that seemed to come from every part of the launch. After a few stunned moments, Tasman picked himself up from the deck where he'd been knocked down. Blood ran from a deep gash in his scalp and a sharp pain in his side told him he'd probably broken a rib or two. Ismail reappeared, apparently none the worse for wear.

They had run into the side of a freighter lying at anchor and riding out the storm.

With aid of ropes, cargo nets and powerful lights, the crew – all Russians – managed to secure the launch alongside and get Tasman and Ismail on board the ship. There they were given dry clothes and hot food, and the freighter's cook cum medical orderly stitched the gash in Tasman's head and bound up his chest.

The Russian captain, who spoke broken English, wondered whether the two men were smugglers or even spies, but finally concluded that they were just stupid – being out in that storm in a launch. Tasman was inclined to agree.

In the morning he and Ismail thanked the crew for their efforts and took the battered but still seaworthy *Mary* out across calm water, heading back to Chanak.

Somehow word of their adventure in the Marmara must have leaked out. A few weeks later a letter arrived from Colonel Hughes, the Imperial War Graves representative in the East and the official who'd sent Tasman out to the Dardanelles back in 1919, without knowing that the young Australian was going there as a man with two missions. The letter from the colonel's Cairo headquarters was blunt: What the bloody hell did Millington think he was doing, running about like a pirate in a Commission boat, flying an Australian flag, and being plucked from the sea by a Russian merchant ship – after he'd run into it!

The colonel went on to say that certain information he'd obtained from sources in London indicated that this wild behaviour of Millington's was nothing new. Apparently the colonel also knew about his Smyrna escapade in 1922 and was aware that he had journeyed among the islands of the northeast Aegean – places that for the most part were not in Turkish territorial waters and had nothing to do with the job of working for the Commission.

Colonel Hughes acknowledged that the wonderful relationship the War Graves Commission had with the Turks was due to Millington's fine work and the rapport he'd set up with the Turkish people over a long period. But what troubled the colonel was that Millington's actions could be interpreted as some sort of clandestine Intelligence operation ... 'as absurd as that may seem!' The letter from Cairo concluded with Colonel Hughes saying that he expected to hear no more reports of strange goings on in which Millington had a part.

The letter worried Tasman. The secretive jaunts he'd made down the Turkish coast and among the islands of the Aegean were his idea alone and not something that had been prompted by the people in London. Ismail, his close friend, knew nothing of what he'd done back then and Tasman had not even mentioned it to his wife. The worrying implication was that London had been keeping tabs on him all the time, and that if London knew about the trips it was reasonable to assume that others did too – people probably a lot closer to home. But who? Tasman decided to be more careful than he had been and to wait and see if there was any evidence of someone spying on the spy.

In view of the colonel's letter, Tasman also decided that he and Ismail would make fewer trips down to Troy to use the transmitter. Puzzled by this, Ismail asked him if the English were no longer interested. Tasman fobbed him off by saying that there wasn't much to report and, besides, he wasn't keen anymore to act as the eyes of people he didn't even know. Ismail gave him a quizzical look but said nothing.

FIVE

The winter of late 1937 came quickly. The dry grass turned white with frost and ice; the trees and shrubs around the graveyards stood frozen at attention in the bleak winds. The numbing silence was disturbed only by the tread of feet as they cracked the rigid earth. So bitter was this winter that Tasman stood down the Commission workers weeks early, but he and Ismail still made the regular trip across the narrows to check on the cemeteries. The bleakness meant an early camp each day, with its warmth of food and fire.

Ismail poured the thick dark coffee that Tasman had come to relish so much – hot and heavily sugared. The familiar aroma filled the tent as they drank from small cups. Tasman had seemed a different man in the months since their Marmara voyage and Ismail could remain silent no longer. Was there some problem?, he asked. Was there anything he could do if there was? Tasman knew that the discovery that someone was reporting on him to London had made him treat everyone, including Ismail, with suspicion. Yet there was no reason to think that Ismail had been monitoring his actions and secretly reporting them. And it suddenly became clear to him that if Ismail wasn't the culprit then there was every chance that the Turk was in far greater danger than he was, because of Ismail's willingness to help him at Troy. Embarrassed at his mistrust of a good friend, Tasman rested an elbow on his swag and told Ismail the whole story, leaving nothing out.

Ismail was so taken aback by what Tasman was telling him that he remained silent until the talking was done and Tasman was awkwardly fumbling with his fourth cigarette. Ismail reached over the low fire, took the makings from Tasman's hands and began to knead the tobacco between his fingers. After a few moments he passed a perfectly rolled cigarette back, saying with a smile that, for such a clever Australian, Tasman made the sort of cigarette a blind old woman would make.

Signs of the thaw and the change of season were slow in coming, but when they did they brought with them confused requests from London for Tasman to pay special attention to any movements by German ships through the Dardanelles. The Intelligence people also asked him to set up a listening and watching post on Cape Helles, near the southern entrance to the Dardanelles, using special equipment they would be sending him in the near future. Tasman knew that the Cape was unsuitable for Intelligence purposes because the area was quite heavily populated, but repeated expressions of concern about the location merely resulted in his being told that London was sending a man out to explain everything. Until then he should go on reporting as usual, but more often. And would he please keep in mind the need to know about German ships!

Tasman tersely replied that he was well aware of the political changes in Europe and particularly in Germany, as he still read the English newspapers, even though they were a week old.

By March 1939 there was still no sign of either the special equipment for Cape Helles or the man who would explain everything. Tasman and Ismail had been spending much of their spare time wandering around the northeast Aegean in the motor launch. On their latest foray they ran up to Suvla Bay in the Gulf of Saros, where Tasman had landed as a soldier with the 26th Battalion in 1915. Both men were deeply affected, once again, by the tragic loss of life that had occurred on the Peninsula.

On their return to Chanak from Suvla, Tasman found a surprise waiting for him in the shape of the mystery man from London. He had arrived the day before. With his hand extended he introduced himself as Smith.

'Not John, I hope!' Tasman said.

The response was curt. 'No, it's not. As a matter of fact it's David – David Smith. I rather gather that you've been expecting me.'

Tasman asked him if he'd like a cup of tea.

'English Breakfast, is it?' said Smith.

'Indian I believe, old chap,' Tasman replied. 'We just have to make do out here, you know.'

Tasman couldn't help but wonder where they'd found this bloke. Smith was utterly British in manner and dress. Tasman made the tea while explaining that he hadn't in fact been expecting anyone at all, given that it was now a year or so since London had told him they were sending someone out. Smith took the cup of tea he was offered and sat down, crossing his legs; his tailored English suit complete with regimental tie made him quite a sight in Tasman's living room.

'There were some difficulties you know, Millington – nothing of any concern, just some difficulties.'

Tasman didn't say anything, half expecting some long and involved story. Finally he asked: 'So then, Dave, why are you here?'

Smith almost dropped his cup. 'It's *David* – if you don't mind, Millington!' Recovering his composure, he told Tasman that he would like to visit Cape Helles the next day to make an expert assessment of it as a location for the listening post. Again his manner riled Tasman, who knew that Cape Helles posed serious problems.

Smith arrived at the waterfront right on time, dressed more for a day's yachting than for anything else. Tasman watched him as he walked down the jetty, stepped on board the Commission boat, tripped, and almost fell into the water.

'Ismail, this is Dave – the bloke I told you about,' Tasman said as he started up the engine.

Ismail cast off the lines and decided it would be better to say nothing.

Within a couple of hours David Smith realised that Tasman was right and London was wrong. What he found at the Cape was not the isolated area he'd expected, with a clear view over both the entrance to the Dardanelles and the Aegean. Instead, as Tasman had reported, the site was quite unsuited to the business of watching and listening. The adjoining Morto Bay – the name meant 'death cove' – was anything but dead. At the village of Seddulbahir lively-looking locals were carrying on the day's work, and even up at the ruins of the old monastery Smith saw farmers in the field.

Tasman didn't expect the sincere apology that followed. Back on the boat he was also given a clear explanation of all the cloak and dagger stuff that had been going on for the past year or more. Turkey was a strategic place, obviously, but the British Government had been slow to see the threat posed by the new Germany; and now with the occupation of Czechoslovakia by German troops there was good reason to think that war in Europe was more than likely. Surrounded to the north by Bulgaria, Romania and Russia, Turkey was sure to be right in the thick of it. The British Prime Minister and even the King himself had been fooled by Germany, but there were those within Intelligence circles who'd not been so naive and who had been gathering information for years. Their sources had included Millington and Ismail as they made their reports on German shipping movements.

Ismail was quick to say that his country would never again side with Germany. The Turks hated war. 'Never again,' he kept saying, 'never again.' Smith agreed, as did Tasman as he put his hand on Ismail's shoulder in a gesture of mateship and support.

The motor launch made its way back to Chanak; it had never seemed to take so long. The thoughts of the three men remained unspoken until they reached the Commission's moorings. Smith then said that Tasman, assisted by Ismail, should continue to watch German shipping in the narrows and make daily reports to London. Tasman pointed out that a trip to Troy every day was impossible. Smith agreed and said that new equipment would arrive in due course that would make the job much easier. Meanwhile, Tasman should do the best he could.

Tasman and Smith parted company a few days later, on much better terms than when they'd first met. As they shook hands, Smith said: 'By the way, Millington, my name's not David, actually.'

Tasman grinned and said he'd guessed that it wasn't.

'It's really John – John Smith – but I always use the name David to make it sound more genuine.'

Tasman was still laughing to himself when Ismail turned up. When told what Smith had said, the Turk failed to see the humour in it, which made Tasman laugh even more.

The expected war was all too soon a reality. On 1 September 1939 the Germans occupied Poland and two days later England and France declared war on Germany. For the second time in only 25 years the sometimes fragile peace of Europe was shattered by the march of the jackboot. The War Graves Commission offered to move Tasman to London to join his wife and son – the boy was now in school there – but Tasman felt his duty was to stay, at least for the moment, and see what developed. Turkey was a neutral country and Tasman saw no problem for either himself or any other Commission employees.

At last a box came from London containing the new radio. Small and compact, it bore no resemblance to the contraption he'd disguised as a 'quake bomb' so long ago. Tasman spent the day installing the new radio under the floor of his kitchen. There was little point in trying to hide it too well – neutral or not, it wouldn't take the Turkish authorities long to discover what he was up to . . . if they wanted to.

The wireless traffic between Chanak and London was hectic from the start. London requested that Tasman watch for any signs of U-boats. Germany's submarines had already proved their deadly worth, as even on the day that war was declared the *U–30* had sunk the liner *Athenia*. The Intelligence people also felt that, with three-quarters of the German merchant fleet trapped in foreign ports, there might be attempts by U-boats to help the ships get back to their home waters. Tasman decided to make a boat trip across the Sea of Marmara, with the intention of going right up into the harbours of Istanbul to gather information about any German merchant ships stuck there. Beyond the Bosporus lay the Black Sea and the gateway to Russia. The intelligence he could gather might well prove vital to London and at least make him feel as though he was doing something rather than sitting around.

Again Tasman and Ismail took the old motor launch, *Mary*, up the narrows and into the Marmara. Fuel was much harder to obtain this time, and the prices higher. They followed the northern shore of the sea, sighting one or two elderly German freighters, which Tasman recorded in his journal. Problems with their engine forced a two-night layover before they approached Istanbul. Five kilometres from the ancient city they began to move in among scores of merchant ships of every size and shape, the cargoes loaded high on the decks, the crews of twenty nations standing idly at bow or stern. Ships trapped by war, their captains unable or unwilling to make a run for it.

Many of these vessels were German, and Tasman worked feverishly at his journal as Ismail guided the *Mary* through the floating steel city.

They went on up the Bosporus as far as the entrance to the Black Sea, then moored for the night. Ismail nearly had a heart attack when he looked out of the cabin and saw Tasman pumping fuel from a drum into the launch's main tank. In the darkness the telltale stream of hot tobacco embers from Tasman's hopeless cigarette was falling around the half open drum.

The Marmara was not the friendliest part of the world, it seemed. On the return journey along the shoreline the engine died – a ruptured fuel line and easy to fix. What wasn't so easy to fix was the discovery that while attending to the engine they had drifted on to rocks lying just offshore. But after an hour or so of rocking the boat vigorously, they managed to free the *Mary* and return to Chanak.

There Tasman wasted no time in reporting to London on everything they'd seen in the way of German merchant ships. London responded by telling

Tasman not to conduct any further 'unauthorised operations'.

'The ungrateful bastards,' Tasman kept repeating to himself when he got off the radio. Ismail recognised immediately that Tasman was in a mood again. The English were back to being 'bloody Pommies' and the Australian's cigarettes spewed ash like tree bark after a lightning strike as Tasman paced the floor of the kitchen.

Ismail sat in silence waiting for a break in the storm. 'Perhaps the Englanders are right, Millington. Perhaps we should just do as they asked and watch for any sign of U-boats in the narrows. War will not come to Turkey, perhaps we should not get involved.'

The moment Ismail paused, he knew he'd said the wrong thing. Tasman stood there red in the face and about to explode. Ismail hurriedly changed tack. 'Or perhaps we should ignore the English order and make a war on Germany ourselves from here in Chanak, Millington. Yes, I think you are right. We will make our own war and I will be most pleased to help you. Would you like that, Millington?'

Tasman was now laughing. Never before had he seen such a fast about-face. 'Yes, Ismail, I like your idea. We'll do something to shorten the war. I don't know what, but we'll do something.'

SIX

In Europe the war grew worse by the day. Belgium, the Netherlands and France fell to the Nazis, who then turned their sights on England. In March 1940 Tasman received new orders: he was going back to war, working more formally for British Intelligence, while maintaining his War Graves role. The balancing act suddenly became a lot harder when he received secret orders from MI6. MI6 needed his expertise with seacraft and had arranged a suitable vessel, the Commission's boats being inadequate for its purposes. But it would be Millington's job, the instructions went on, to modify the vessel to his requirements and provide a trustworthy crew. There would be further orders, he was told. Tasman was baffled by this. How on earth could London expect him to find a crew and, more to the point, how many men would be needed? What sort of craft were they talking about? How could he even begin to hide it? Ismail, when he heard about it, was far more interested in what London wanted them to do with it.

Later that month there was another surprise. There on Tasman's doorstep, with a big smile on his face, was John Smith. The Englishman said that he'd been sent out to help Millington set things up.

'What things would they be?' asked Tasman.

Smith was baffled – Millington seemed to know nothing about MI6's plans for him. 'Didn't you get orders?' he asked.

Tasman just grunted and said: 'Orders, orders! Mushrooms don't get orders!'

Tension and confusion over the whole situation were something that Smith didn't need. Millington had been singled out as a key man, not only because of his geographic location and seagoing expertise but also because of the high regard the Turks had for him. Smith had orders too: say nothing that the man doesn't need to know. But with Millington completely in the dark, Smith had no choice but to tell him everything he knew. And time was running short.

British Intelligence, Smith said, had agents in Italy who had little doubt that the Fascist dictator Benito Mussolini, whom Hitler had been courting for years, was making plans to enter the war. It was now a question of when, not if. Tasman remarked that none of the Italians he'd ever known had struck him as warlike people, even if Roman history suggested otherwise. But Smith was very sure of his facts. Tasman listened intently as he went on. The Italians had invaded Albania in April the previous year, but wouldn't be content with that because of Mussolini's massive ego. Available intelligence indicated that the Italians were going to be a major problem in the Mediterranean, with the odds heavily in favour of the Italian Navy. It had faster and far more modern warships than Britain had and the British naval bases couldn't expect much help from home either, given the full-blown war raging in the Atlantic. The desperate position in which Britain found itself clearly meant that its ships at Alexandria, Gibraltar and Malta were on their own in more ways than one.

Smith was filling in a lot of blanks for Tasman but he still hadn't touched on what London wanted from the Australian. Tasman remained patient while Smith gradually moved the mushroom into the daylight. British agents in Italy, although certain of that country's moves to enter the war, remained unclear as to where the action would begin. The only thing certain was that Italy would be alone in whatever it did, Germany being preoccupied elsewhere.

Smith was silent for some time and then came to the point about Tasman's role – or at least its broad outline. Final orders and details would follow. 'Two days from now,' Smith said, 'a boat will be made available. We'll need to go and get it ourselves, I'm afraid. We have to be off Limnos Island at 1930 hours for the pick-up.'

Tasman interrupted him: 'What type of boat, and who's bringing it?'

Smith said that British Intelligence had got the navy to hand over an MTB, a motor torpedo boat, along with some special equipment that might prove handy. 'All the normal surface armaments have been removed,' he added. 'Don't want to make too much of a fuss – the Turks might think you're part of the war effort!' Smith laughed in a way that always annoyed Tasman.

His head now spinning, Tasman said: 'Smith, do you have any idea at all what those cronies of yours in London are asking? This is Turkey – neutral Turkey. I'm here by the grace of the Turks. I'm the representative of the Imperial War Graves

Commission. Using radios and watching for German U-boats is one thing, but gunboats – gunboats! Are you all out of your mind?'

Smith replied that it wasn't a gunboat at all. 'There are no deck guns, Millington. No guns, no gunboat.'

Tasman got up, walked out of the house and headed down to the waterfront, where Ismail was painting the hull of a Commission boat. Ismail was strangely calm about the news, saying that all would be well and that between them they would find a way to keep the big boat a secret. 'And don't forget, Millington, we made our decision to play war before your London people told us how we should play it.'

Ismail returned with Tasman to the house, where Smith waited, half expecting that the Australian would refuse to carry out the orders from MI6. He was clearly relieved when Tasman came through the door and asked what needed to be done in the two days before the rendezvous with the navy people. The motor torpedo boat was coming under escort from Gibraltar, and Tasman began to grasp the importance that MI6 placed on his coming operations.

Ismail said he would go down to the *Mary* at once and start preparations for the trip to Limnos while Tasman and Smith made plans. Tasman was impressed with Smith when he told Ismail that he was under no obligation to get involved. Ismail gave a cheeky smile and said he thought it was a bit too late now – he'd been involved for years.

The island of Limnos lies about 100 kilometres southwest of Chanak. The point of interception with the MTB and its escort was twenty kilometres south of the island. The navy escort had orders to wait for only an hour beyond the appointed time of 1930 hours. If the rendezvous failed they were to get out of there. So there was no room for error in Tasman's navigation.

He and Smith had agreed that the torpedo boat could not be brought back to Chanak. It was Ismail who provided the answer. Over dinner that night he reminded Tasman of the sea trip they'd taken around the coast of the Peninsula to a small and isolated inlet at the top of Suvla Bay, a perfect place to hide a boat. Pleased with the idea, Tasman calculated that from the pick-up point south of Limnos it was a distance of 170 kilometres to Suvla, and by going around the eastern side of Gokceada Island he could keep the

MTB within Turkish territorial (and neutral) waters much of the way. Yes, Ismail's idea was brilliant. John Smith agreed.

The three men decided that Tasman and Ismail would take the MTB up to Suvla, and that Smith would take the *Mary* back to Gelibolu on the Peninsula, up the narrows beyond Chanak, and wait for Tasman and Ismail to trek the 30 kilometres overland. All three of them would then take the *Mary* back to Chanak as though nothing had happened. Tasman also went over an alternative plan in case the MTB ran into bother. His choice was to deliberately sink it as close to land as possible, paddle ashore, and try not to be taken prisoner by anyone. If they were, they'd deny everything and hope for the best.

Two worries remained in Tasman's mind. The first was how he would go in handling a strange vessel much larger than the Commission boats. Secondly, while the Commission boats were powered by small engines, and a single drum of fuel would take the *Mary* a long way, an MTB with its powerful engines needed a lot of fuel. Smith had been told that the navy would be leaving petrol in drums aboard the MTB and that further supplies would be arranged. He shared Tasman's concerns but trusted that MI6 had the matter in hand.

Finally, Tasman radioed London to say that all was ready at his end.

Just before 1930 hours Tasman switched off the launch's motor. As he did so they heard the rumble of big engines far across the calm sea. The sound grew by the minute until a massive shape loomed up almost on top of them, the engine noise dying to a dull throb. A searchlight suddenly illuminated the *Mary*, half blinding Tasman and reducing the launch's bow and masthead lamps to mere candles. A voice from high above called for Millington and instructed him to hold his boat in its present position: 'There is a vessel coming astern of you!' Moments later the afterdeck of the *Mary* was dwarfed by the bow of the motor torpedo boat as it nudged alongside. Another voice called out to them to secure the line which was thrown by a seaman down to where Ismail was standing. The side of the MTB glanced against the *Mary* and, grabbing the line, Ismail tied off quickly on a cleat.

The first thing they saw was that the MTB's deck space was covered in petrol drums. The whole craft was a floating bomb. 'Put out that bloody fag, mate!'

said an abrupt voice aboard the MTB. 'You'll blow us all to hell.'

Another seaman felt for the *Mary*'s gunwale with his foot, then jumped down on to the light-flooded deck. 'Which one of you is Tasman Millington?' he asked.

'That's me,' said Tasman. They shook hands.

The young sailor went on: 'Well, she's all yours. There's almost eighteen hundred gallons of petrol in drums, and the ship refuelled the tanks less than two hours ago. Everything else is down below. So, good luck, sir!'

Four other men had lowered themselves on to the *Mary*. One of them had a torch and signalled the ship, now lying half a kilometre off. A few minutes later a small shoreboat rushed up alongside, the men boarded it and were gone. In the diminished illumination of the searchlight Tasman and Ismail wasted no time in scrambling up on the MTB, with Smith standing by to cast off the line from the *Mary* as soon as they were ready. As the navy ship turned away, the only light now was that coming from the *Mary*'s own lamps.

Tasman and Ismail spent a few minutes familiarising themselves with the MTB and its controls. Smith had cast off and was steering a course back to the Dardanelles, the *Mary*'s silhouette fading fast in the night. Tasman tentatively pushed the MTB's throttles forward and the big twin petrol engines roared to life; a little more throttle and the bow lifted as the boat rapidly gathered speed even with the weight of the fuel drums lashed down on deck. Tasman pointed the bow to the northeast. Between Limnos and the mouth of the Dardanelles they re-entered Turkish waters; a heading west of the Peninsula would now take them close to Gokceada on the way to Suvla.

Ismail went below to see what 'equipment' the navy had left with them. Some time later he appeared beside Tasman, looking wide-eyed. 'Millington, I think your English wish us to make war by ourselves!' he said. Tasman asked him what he was talking about. 'See for yourself, Millington. I will steer the boat.'

Tasman didn't believe his eyes at first. The below-decks space was filled with weapons and ammunition boxes. There were sub-machine guns by the dozen, old Lewis guns, Bren and Vickers guns, handguns and grenades. What was London expecting? Included in the arsenal were enough explosives and detonators to blow up the whole of the Aegean – or the MTB if they got a spark among them. There and then Tasman swore off cigarettes until they reached Suvla.

John Smith was making a much slower journey in the *Mary* and with his limited knowledge of boats was busy keeping an eye on the compass and an ear to the engine. He found himself going over the procedures he'd been given, as a schoolboy might go over his arithmetic tables. Unlike Tasman, he had no idea when he crossed back into Turkish waters. Smith assumed that in due course he would see the coast, and a glance at his watch told him it shouldn't be far off. Less than twenty minutes later he sighted the dim shoreline but, as the *Mary* motored closer, the break around the headland that he'd been expecting was not there. There was no entrance to the Dardanelles to be seen. He must have drifted further south with the current, he decided, but how far south he didn't know. The shoreline ahead could be the potentially disastrous Trojan coast.

Smith lashed the wheel to stop it turning and went below to look at the chart, then raced back to the helm. Turning to the north, he worked the *Mary* inshore as far as he dared and moved up the coast until, by the grace of Poseidon he reached the mouth of the narrows. From there, he thought to himself, it would be plain sailing all the way to Gelibolu.

Shortly before daylight Tasman eased the bow of the MTB into the small inlet known as Suvla Cove and shut down the engines. Ismail set about securing the anchors and then fastened the lines to what was left of an old pier, which hadn't been used since the 11th Division embarked from it during the war before this one. There was little time to be lost but the only thing on Tasman's mind was having a smoke. He darted across the rotting jetty and sprang to the ground, moving well away from the boat and pulling out his tobacco pouch. Ismail soon joined him and they sat on the rocks contemplating the torpedo boat.

Given the state of the pier, the need to get the petrol drums off the deck and hidden away, and the need to do something to the MTB to drastically change its appearance, Tasman and Ismail knew they'd have to get help. Smith's assistance alone wouldn't be enough. But for the moment the MTB was fairly safe in this isolated place.

Collecting their gear, they began to make their way over the rugged peninsula to rejoin Smith who'd be waiting at Gelibolu. Late that afternoon they spotted the *Mary* resting alongside the wharf at the old Commission headquarters. Smith had been watching for them and gave a wave the moment they came into sight. They were heading back over the narrows to Chanak when Tasman enquired whether Smith had had any problems getting the *Mary* home. The Englishman looked a bit sheepish and didn't answer. Tasman glanced at Ismail and they both broke into a laugh as Chanak came into sight in the distance.

SEVEN

Each passing day brought worse news of the war. Germany had invaded the Low Countries in early May of 1940, Rotterdam had been bombed and the Netherlands had surrendered, Amiens had fallen and Nazi armoured divisions were approaching Dunkirk. Within days Boulogne-sur-Mer fell, followed by Calais, and the evacuation of British forces began from Dunkirk on the 27th.

Orders from London were slow in coming for Tasman – understandably, as the war was elsewhere at that moment and Germany seemed to be unstoppable. The day after Norway surrendered, Italy entered the war and within 24 hours attacked Malta by air. The war suddenly came much nearer and, orders or no orders, Millington decided to wait no longer. Ismail and even Smith agreed that they had to act on their own accord.

The first thing they needed was manpower, and that was something Tasman had a lot of. Over the years the Commission had been employing Russian workers, men who could now no longer return home. They could be brought on side, but Tasman would be taking a huge chance in telling them about the MTB – yet it was only option he had. In the end he needn't have worried. They volunteered to a man and swore themselves to secrecy, perhaps seeing it as their only way of striking back at the Nazis. Whatever the Superintendent wanted them to do, they said, he could rely on them to carry out his orders just as they did in the war cemeteries. The Turkish workers were left out of it completely, more for their own good than anything else – in case they were caught or even suspected of assisting an Australian, working for British Intelligence in a neutral country, who happened to have a motor torpedo boat and a vast amount of firepower! Tasman decided not to think about the possible consequences.

The problem with the navy MTB was that it looked like a navy MTB, and if it was going to be involved in operations that would have to change. The

Turks had many large fishing boats, very colourful craft painted in bright reds, greens and yellows. They could be seen quite clearly from a long way off and the long strings of sponges and nets hanging from the stubby sailing masts combined to make the exact shape of the boats hard to discern until you were close to them. Tasman wanted his MTB to look just like a 'minding my own business' Turkish fishing boat.

Ismail had a cousin, and the cousin had a shed full of paint and that paint, along with other materials, found its way on to the launch on the morning Ismail picked up Tasman and Smith to go over to the Peninsula. The Russian workers were waiting for them when the *Mary* slipped into the dock. Tasman had an announcement to make: Paris had fallen to the enemy. If any man was unsure about the task, now was the time to back away; no one would think the worse of him for doing so. None of the workers took up the offer.

Even with carts and barrows it was a long, hard slog getting the tools, paint, timber and camouflage material over to Suvla. Night came before they set up camp in the desolate cove. Tasman, Ismail and Smith were exhausted but no sooner had they started a fire than they heard the sound of hammering coming from the old pier. The Russians were already hard at work building new decking. Throughout the night, with only a few old kerosene lamps for light, they built a strong platform on the ruins of the piles. When dawn came they wrestled the petrol drums off the MTB and rolled them ashore. There seemed no stopping their self-imposed labour, until Tasman forced them to rest and turned his attention to the MTB.

The superstructure above the deck had to be altered almost to the point of removing it and a wheelhouse had to be constructed in the manner of those on fishing boats. The fake mast looked authentic and, finally, with most of the MTB adorned with cane baskets and nets, even Ismail agreed that the boat would pass muster. During the third day in camp the Russians completed the paint job, producing a carnival of colour and deception. Tasman was more than pleased.

The petrol drums, along with hoses and hand pumps, found a home among the rocks, while an old water tank placed there by soldiers during the Great War began service again, as a weapons and ammunition store.

Back in Chanak Tasman radioed London regarding progress with the boat. London acknowledged the message and then, in what seemed like an afterthought, said: 'You are promoted to Major. Congratulations!' Tasman was surprised and gratified.

'Major Millington ... Yes, sir! ... Immediately, sir! ... A cup of tea, sir?' Ismail paced back and forth in Tasman's lounge room with his hand held in a mock salute.

John Smith watched in amusement. 'Let me be the next to congratulate you, Major Millington,' Smith said, and shook his hand firmly.

Ismail then stepped forward and offered his own hand, saying: 'Damned good show, old chap. Makes me fancy a gin and tonic!' The mimicking of Smith's very proper English accent sent the three of them into riotous laughter.

In the absence of orders from London, Tasman returned to his War Graves duties, much to the relief of the man who stood in for him as and when required. But the MTB was never off Tasman's mind. It would need at least one more crewmember to make it operational. The problem was to find such a man.

During the transformation of the MTB at Suvla one of his Russian workers, a man named Joseph, had shown great interest in the boat, asking intelligent questions about the engines and the instruments. He could be the right man.

Later on Joseph sat in Tasman's kitchen with a cup of coffee in his hands, listening intently as he was told what would be expected from him if he chose to join the crew. Tasman couldn't give him any real details because there were so far none to give him, but he didn't hold back in portraying the grim outcome that might await them. Then Ismail emphasised the paramount need for secrecy, making it clear that they could all be shot if they were taken prisoner by the enemy. 'The enemy is everywhere outside Turkey, and perhaps inside Turkey as well,' Ismail said.

As it turned out, Joseph was experienced with boats – his father and grandfather, both fishermen on the Black Sea, had taught him well. He was quick to volunteer. Tasman said that his first job would be to guard the boat, and to do that he'd have to be permanently in camp by himself at lonely Suvla Cove. Once a week Tasman would send supplies and in the meantime Joseph would run the engines regularly to recharge the batteries.

Orders finally came for both Tasman and Smith. It was early in October 1940 and the British agents in Italy were sure that Mussolini would order an invasion of Greece in weeks or perhaps days. Smith was instructed to go to Greece and Tasman was to get him there. They were to act without delay. Tasman's deputy at Chanak would have additional duties once more.

They prepared well for the trip. Ismail went ahead to Suvla to get the MTB ready and to tell Joseph that they'd joined the war. Tasman came a few hours later with Smith after they'd devised a plan to land him near Kimi on the Greek island of Evvoia. Smith would then cross the island to Khalkis and move down to Athens, where MI6 wanted him to go. The sea crossing from Suvla to Kimi was a little over 300 kilometres, most of it well away from any prying Aegean islands. Tasman estimated that it would take six hours to get Smith to Kimi and another six hours to get the boat back to Suvla at full speed. The prospect of trying to get him any closer to Athens was out of the question because of the unknown factors involved. But John Smith was fluent in Greek, and Tasman consoled himself that he'd be all right after the drop-off.

With everything arranged, the MTB, throttles wide open, made fast passage toward Greece. Ismail had brought weapons and ammunition – 'just in case' – and offered Smith a small automatic pistol. Smith shook his head, saying that if he were caught and searched the war might be over for him. The Greek coast came into sight covered in a pall of mist and sea spray and when, two kilometres out, Tasman slowed the engines to a rumble Ismail and Joseph ran forward to watch for a good spot to land John Smith. The key to putting him ashore was to have him swim the last hundred metres or so with his clothes in a rubber bag. As Tasman brought the MTB broadside to the rocks Smith gave a small wave and lowered himself over the side. The others shouted 'Good luck' as he swam in. Tasman powered up the engines and pointed the boat out to sea again, looking back just long enough to see Smith safely ashore.

The return journey was also uneventful, and when coffee was poured back in Suvla Cove there was a sigh of relief. 'Mind you,' said Tasman, 'we can't always expect to get off so lightly!' Ismail and Joseph understood what he meant.

It transpired that the British agents had been right. Tasman learned from the radio that at the end of October Italy had attacked Greece and that within a few days British forces had been sent to the island of Crete. The Greeks were fighting the Italians over on the Albanian front. For Tasman the war was only a boat trip away.

Mussolini had chosen a fierce enemy in the Greeks, as he soon found out. The Greeks fought as though they were legions of Spartan warriors and attacked the invaders from the moment they crossed the border. More than 125 000 Italian troops swarmed over the frontier, where two Greek forces stood in defence of their homeland. Tasman and Ismail listened daily to BBC reports of the mighty struggle across the waters, and at the allotted time each day Tasman would switch on his radio and listen for further orders from London. But for weeks the radio remained silent.

High in the mountains of northern Greece the Italians were fighting a battle they couldn't win, against an army that was far smaller but whose soldiers fought with courage and passion. The tiny army drove the Italian forces back into Albania, and less than a month after Mussolini's troops first crossed into Greece they were running in retreat with the Greeks at their heels. By the end of the year over 20 000 of Italy's soldiers had soaked the soil of Greece with their blood. The Greek warriors had slaughtered the invaders en masse wherever they found them. The Greeks took a further 26 000 Italians prisoner, while 60 000 more were wounded or suffered the effects of frostbite.

Benito Mussolini, who styled himself 'the new Caesar', was humiliated. His Roman legions cowered and crawled their way home. Tasman thought the news was good in the extreme but didn't for a moment let himself think that the tide of the war had turned. He and Ismail remained alert for anything, which was just as well because Tasman now received a signal from MI6 in London to be wary of German agents or members of Abwehr, the Nazi Military Intelligence organisation. London knew that they were running an espionage station in Turkey – and Chanak would be an ideal place for it.

EIGHT

Ismail burst through the door, panting heavily and trying to catch his breath. He told Tasman he'd overheard a man at the post office asking questions about the War Graves officer and where he could be found.

'He wouldn't be the first visitor to Chanak who was looking for me,' said Tasman.

Ismail replied: 'But he is the first one who speaks with a German accent! Even if he's trying to cover it up.'

Tasman paused a moment. 'How do you know he's a German? Are you sure about the accent?'

Ismail grinned – a long-familiar grin he gave whenever Tasman was wrong about something. 'You forget, Millington, I had much to do with the Germans in the big war when you and I were enemies. You can trust me, the stranger is German and he asks about you. It is most fortunate that he doesn't ask about me, so I may observe him without him knowing.'

'I'm not so sure you're right,' Tasman started to say, when Ismail interrupted him.

'I will be most pleased to kill him for you, Millington. I will butcher the spying dog and feed him to the wolves!'

Tasman was taken aback by Ismail's offer, and said: 'No, definitely not!' Ismail was a good man and a loyal friend, but he could also be exasperating. 'You are not going to kill the man, my friend,' said Tasman. 'You will watch him, find out where he's staying, and then we will decide who and what he is.'

Ismail gave him a mocking salute of acceptance, but said: 'Understood, though you will be sorry if we do not kill him now.' Ismail left and headed into Chanak, intent on proving that he was right. He was sure the German was an Abwehr agent.

Ismail's search took him to a small hotel and café down on the waterfront. The stranger he'd seen that day at the post office sat at a table with another man, drinking coffee and engaged in what appeared to be small talk. One of them pointed at the constant flow of fish baskets being brought up from the harbour to the street, where merchants mixed with crowds of haggling customers. The two men sat there well into the evening as Ismail watched them. They drank more coffee, ordered food, then smoked cigarettes. Eventually they got up from the table and went upstairs to their rooms. Ismail waited until the lights had gone out, then rushed back to Tasman's house. 'Millington, Millington, there are two of them and one is certain to be a German – he eats like a pig!'

Tasman stood there, aghast at Ismail's idea of logic. 'So you think we should kill them because one eats like a pig? That's enough proof they're Nazi spies? Anyway, where are these Abwehr agents of yours now?' He waited for an answer.

Finally Ismail said: 'They have gone up to their rooms in the hotel!'

Tasman laughed. 'And I suppose they're up there sending coded signals to Berlin right now!'

Ismail frowned. 'I had not allowed for that, Millington, but it is possible.'

Tasman said he'd let London know the situation at the usual time next day. He'd already decided to ask for orders before anything was done. Ismail left, a little calmer, but still not convinced he wasn't right.

Tasman contacted London as he'd said he would and, after giving the details to the radio operator, was surprised to be instructed to stand by. Within a few minutes a long series of names and descriptive details came through regarding known agents, not only of the German Abwehr but also Italians in the service of the SIM, the Servizio Informazione Militaire, Mussolini's own Intelligence people, who were working closely with the Nazis.

Tasman decided not to divulge this information to Ismail just yet. The Turk was seeing too many enemy spies around every corner and Tasman felt that if he revealed what London had said, no foreigner in the whole of Chanak would be safe.

A day or two later there was a loud pounding on his door. It was Ismail. 'I was right, Millington. They are enemy agents – one German and the other Italian. You wanted proof, I have proof!' He handed Tasman a black, leatherbound notebook. Inside it were pencil sketches of Chanak, detailed drawings of the Turkish military areas and a short list of names, which included Millington's. The middle pages were a jumble of numbers, which meant nothing to Tasman except for the fact that the writing down the page sides was in German.

Ismail explained that he'd broken into the men's

hotel rooms after they'd left the harbour on a small fishing boat.

'You believe me now, Millington?' he asked. 'There is more. They travel as Dutch merchant seamen and they have passports — Dutch passports.' Ismail was on to something after all, Tasman realised. 'There is another thing, Millington. One of them has a suitcase and inside it is a radio.'

Tasman apologised for not taking Ismail's advice earlier and then confessed that London had warned him of enemy Intelligence agents only the day before. 'But how do you know one of them is an Italian?' he asked.

'In his room he has a picture on the dresser — an oldish woman dressed in black and certain to be his "Dutch mother". Well, his old "Dutch mother" is holding a figure of the Madonna and standing in front of the Vatican in Rome. The man is Italian, Millington. He is more Italian than Mussolini himself!'

There was now a very real threat to Tasman's operations. The transmitter under the floor, the motor torpedo boat on the other side of the Peninsula along with fuel and weapons, the Russian workers who knew it was there, the Turkish military – all this meant that he needed to act quickly to avoid discovery. And the notebook had to be returned to the hotel room before it was found to be missing. Tasman carefully copied out every entry and asked Ismail to take the notebook back.

Ismail reappeared before long bearing the news that he hadn't been able to replace the book because the German was in his room. However, the two agents would be going down for a meal in a while and there was a good chance that the German wouldn't first check under the mattress, where he'd hidden the notebook. Ismail said he might be able to sneak the book back then.

Tasman decided to create a diversion by having a meal himself at the café and, if need be, engaging the men in conversation to give Ismail plenty of time. There was no other choice, Ismail agreed. Two hours later Tasman sat down at one of the small round tables outside the hotel. There was no sign of either man and he ordered coffee. Ismail was across the street and from where he stood he had a clear view of the café. Soon the two men came down and seated themselves at a table near Tasman.

Ismail could now see that the plan was doomed to failure. Millington hadn't allowed for the hotel's owner, his wife and two daughters, who were moving in and out of the kitchen area and would see anyone trying to go upstairs. Before he could think of his next move the taller of the two men began to speak with Tasman, who almost immediately rose to his feet and joined the strangers at their table.

A further diversion was needed. Ismail looked around, thinking. An army truck was parked further up the road and there was no sign of its driver. Ismail decided that chaos was the answer. He went to the truck, got in, released the brakes and let the vehicle roll toward the café. The truck knocked down the small railing that enclosed the area and ran into the tables – just moments after Tasman and the two men leapt out of the way in a single move. The hotel owner and his family were outside in an instant, debris still falling from the canopy overhead. Everyone stood around the truck, looking for its army driver.

Tasman saw Ismail heading down to the harbour an hour or two later. 'Where have you been, Ismail? I was almost killed at the café by a runaway army truck!'

His arms upstretched, Ismail jumped for joy. 'Millington, I am so glad you were not injured ... I could think of nothing else. Are the two spies dead, Millington?'

Tasman suddenly saw that the incident had been Ismail's doing. 'You're mad,' he shouted. 'A mad bastard! You could have killed me.'

A few seconds passed. 'But did I kill the spies, Millington?'

Tasman didn't answer. He turned and walked off to the boathouse, with Ismail following well out of reach.

He didn't stay angry with Ismail for long. At the boathouse the Turk told him that during all the confusion at the café, he had managed to put the notebook back in the hotel room. Tasman later radioed London and made his report on the two men and the information contained in the book, only to be told that he would have to wait – the officer looking after such things was unavailable! But Tasman sent the signal again, insisting on orders right there and then, to which London replied that he should feel free to use his own judgment.

The regular tour of the war graves was a week overdue and Tasman made it clear to Ismail that he wanted him to come to the Peninsula with him, saying that they should also use the opportunity to check on the MTB and Joseph, who'd be in need of some company after living at Suvla on his own. But in fact Tasman wanted to make sure that Ismail didn't shoot, strangle or poison the two agents while he was gone. He wanted to know where Ismail was night and day. As for the agents, well, he'd decide what to do when they returned from the Peninsula.

Lone Pine, the Hellspit and Shrapnel Valley, Johnston's Jolly, Quinn's Post, Baby 700 and the Nek – Tasman knew them all like the back of his hand.

The most northern of the Commission's gravesites was Azmak cemetery. The word 'isolation' didn't describe it. Here the graves registration unit had found the remains of Lt Col. Proctor-Beauchamp and 180 of his men, the so-called 'Lost Army of Gallipoli'. But they weren't 'lost', they were all killed. There were 1074 graves in the stillness of Azmak and 684 of them belonged to unknown soldiers.

Many years had come and gone and many things had happened. Yet it was always an emotional sight when now and then the earthbound remains of a soldier of the Great War decided to reveal themselves, as they did early one morning on Tasman's tour.

'Millington, there is a badge here ... he is a New Zealander!'

Tasman crouched down as Ismail gently lifted the dark and crusted metal emblem from the soil in the open hollow. Tasman took it and examined it carefully while Ismail softly scraped away the earth from which it had come. The Turk had learned the routine long ago and knew that Tasman always insisted on making a meticulous search of any site in the hope of finding the soldier's name. They first searched for metals – buckles, buttons, badges, perhaps the rusted part of a rifle. Then they looked for anything else that could prevent another stone marker from bearing the simple words: 'A soldier of the Great War.' Tasman had often said that he never felt he'd done his best unless every possible effort was made to give a hero back his name. It was the very least that could be accorded him. But now, after such a long time, the task was more often than not impossible.

'Millington, there is nothing more – he is known only to God.'

Tasman stood up, and as he did so gave a deep sigh. 'Thanks,' he said, reaching down to grasp Ismail's hand and pulling him up from the hollow.

'Millington, we will make a cover over him tonight. Tomorrow we will bury him with his mates.' Ismail, too, would have liked to know the name of this man, his former enemy, but it was not to be.

The evening, when it came, closed in slowly over their work camp. The heat of the fire sent embers soaring high into the air as Tasman's party of workers settled in for the night. It would be a long night – it always was before a morning burial. Earlier in the day Tasman had sent a Turkish worker to collect the items needed to inter the remains: canvas to encase the bones, sail thread to seal the shroud, a New Zealand flag to cover it, and ropes to lower the soldier down to eternal rest among other fallen warriors.

Long before sunrise Tasman and Ismail made their way in the light of a hurricane lamp to the hollow and the covered remains at the bottom of it. Ismail climbed down while Tasman laid out the canvas on the ground above. And there, under the lamp light, Ismail carefully passed up all that was left of someone's son. Just as carefully, Tasman placed the bones on the canvas sheet in a semblance of the human structure they once were.

There is a coldness that descends in the hour before sunrise. Tasman and Ismail could feel it brush over them as they carried the flag-draped New Zealander across a low rise and into the cemetery. They moved past six rows of graves until they reached the newly made place that the workers had dug the previous afternoon. The workers had come to the ceremony and each of them placed a sprig of rosemary on the centre of the flag, then stood back.

The charcoal sky gradually gave way to the dawn as a new day emerged over Gallipoli. Tasman began reading the burial service. There would be no Last Post – there was no bugler to sound it. There were no comrades to stand at attention. No family to mourn the loss. There were just Tasman and Ismail and a few workers to see that the decent thing was done.

The ropes bore the remains down to the bottom of the grave and were then withdrawn as Tasman, followed by Ismail, stepped forward and scattered a handful of dirt over a New Zealand son. As workers began filling in the site, Tasman took a piece of paper from the Bible in his hand and studied it for a moment before reading aloud: 'These by the Dardanelles laid down their shining youth in battle and won fair renown for their native land so that their enemy groaned carrying war's harvest from the field, but for themselves they found a deathless monument of valour.'

Tasman had long admired these words, appropriate as they were. Eerily, they'd been penned by a scribe of ancient Greece, five centuries before Christ.

Two days later, Tasman and Ismail pushed on to Suvla Cove. From the top of the hill they could see

Joseph by the pier and the motor torpedo boat calm at its lines. In the evening the Russian broke out a rum issue that he'd discovered while exploring a dry well on the cliff at the site of the old 9th Corps Headquarters. Tasman was interested in just how much rum he'd found, and Joseph proudly showed him three barrels, one of them now half empty. He'd come across them weeks before. Being at least 26 years old, the rum was very, very smooth.

A week spent on the Gallipoli Peninsula was a long time when the whole world seemed to be at war. Victories one day, defeats the next, give and take, win and lose – regardless of how Tasman heard the latest BBC news it wasn't good. The fact was clear: Germany would follow the Italians into Greece at some point, a move that Hitler had not intended before but, now that Mussolini had botched the job, Germany needed to protect its interests in that part of the world by doing the work itself.

Back in Chanak, Ismail reminded Tasman that there was still an urgent job for him too. The enemy agents were alive and well and living in the town.

Tasman decided to take things into his own hands. A few days later he went to the hotel and asked to speak with the tall 'Dutch seaman', who promptly came downstairs. Over coffee in the remains of the outside café, Tasman invited the man and his friend to join him the next day aboard the Commission's boat for a little sightseeing down the narrows. He said it was the very least he could offer them as strangers to Chanak, caught up as they were by the small problem of a war. The man accepted eagerly and they agreed to meet at the moorings the following morning.

Ismail was unsure about the plan unfolded for him later that day. Tasman had decided that, whatever they were up to, the two agents must be prevented at any cost from finding out about his operations and the MTB over in Suvla. Both must be silenced and, as he was in charge, the task must fall to him.

'Millington, you will forgive me,' Ismail said. 'You have not fired a gun in more than a quarter of a century. I think they may not hesitate when you might!'

Tasman nodded, but remained insistent that he would take the two men out on the boat alone. Ismail left Tasman to his thoughts and returned to his own house, where his family now lived with him in Chanak. He ate a late meal with his wife, then hurriedly headed down to the harbour.

The demons danced in Tasman's mind throughout the quiet hours. The small pistol, an automatic, grew warm in his hand as he held it, loading the magazine and pushing it into the butt with his fingers then pulling back the slide and knowing it was ready to fire. He'd killed the enemy before – from afar and long ago. Now the enemy to be killed were men that only yesterday he'd spoken to. Was it duty? War? Or murder? All three? In his troubled state of mind Tasman hardly noticed the darkness lift from Chanak.

There was a knock on the door and a sudden rush of light as the door opened wide. Tasman instinctively reached for the gun beside him, stood up and pointed it at the doorway. There stood the agent thought to be the Italian, with Ismail holding a sub-machine gun to the man's side. 'Millington, there has been a change to your plan!' the Turk said.

Tasman pushed past them and looked outside, praying that they hadn't been seen. But the area was quiet and he couldn't see anyone. 'What's happened, Ismail?' he asked. He noticed that the Italian was standing at attention, a silly-looking grin on his face.

'I am Captain Gino di Steffano, a former officer in the Italian Army. For me the war is ended, and may I say that I am very pleased to be your prisoner, Colonel.'

'Major,' Tasman said.

'No, Colonel, I am only a captain.'

'No, Captain, *I* am a major!'

'Yes, Colonel. I am pleased to be your prisoner, sir.'

The conversation was becoming as silly as the man's grin. Tasman looked at Ismail. 'Are you going to say something?'

The Turk smiled. 'Millington, I have killed the German for you!'

As Ismail spoke, the Italian turned his head and spat on Tasman's floor. 'German dog! I am glad he is dead,' the captain remarked, with a look of disgust on his face.

Tasman turned to Ismail, who had some explaining to do.

The three of them sat down to coffee in the kitchen, in an atmosphere both civilised and surreal. The Italian was soon being called Gino, and even filled their cups.

Ismail coughed. 'Millington – the Nazi. He will be no more trouble.'

Gino was just about to spit on the floor again when Tasman stopped him. He was getting impatient, and said: 'Ismail, what the hell is going on?'

After a long pause, the story came out. Ismail had been worried that Tasman could be killed by the agents if things went wrong, so early in the morning he'd gone to the hotel and told the German that he

Tasman Millington.
Australian, Anzac, soldier,
sailor, reluctant spy.
(*Reveille*, 1934)

Australians and New Zealanders on the attack at Anzac Cove.
(National Archives of Australia)

Alliance. Sultan Mehmet V of Turkey greets the Kaiser in 1917.

'The enemy is listening, so be careful on the phone!' This German poster from World War I shows one of the great changes in modern warfare. The radio became a vital tool, and listening in to your enemy became a vital job. (*Illustrated London News*)

A wounded soldier being carried through the endless mud of Flanders in August 1917. By 6 November, when General Haig's troops occupied the ruins of Passchendaele, around 265,000 British soldiers had been killed or wounded in Flanders and only eight kilometres of muddy ground had been gained.

P.B. 190850.

TO IOAN. P.B 103.
GALLIPOLI PENINSULA.

Casualty Form.— Active Service.

Regiment or Corps _W. Coy. 26. Battalion_

Regimental No. _1146_ Rank _Bugle_ Name _Millington Tasman,_

Enlisted (a) _23.4.15_ Terms of Service (a) _Won a ... duration_ Service reckons from (x) _23.4.15_

Date of promotion to present rank } Date of appointment to lance rank } Numerical position on roll of ... 9s. } _117._

Re-engaged Extended

EMBARKED FROM AUSTRALIA JUN 29 1915 N° 128/40 21

Report		Record of promotions, reductions, transfers, casualties, etc., during active service, as reported on Army Form B. 213, Army Form A. 36, or in other official documents. The authority to be quoted in each case	Place	Date	Remarks taken from Army Form B. 213, Army Form A. 36, or other official documents.
Date	From whom received				
27.1.15	C/O	P.V.D. Transferred to Mudros	Anzac		0810 37/134 B212 3.10.15 14.10.15
10.10.15	H.S. Assaye	B.H.O Dismissed Hospital Astma. ex. Convoy	Malta	10.11.15	0810 423/134 A36 ... 28.10.15
2.10.15	3rd Aus Gen Hosp 143	B.H.O Admitted & dangerously Mon sparca fish to Mudros	Anzac	2.10.15	0810 43/145 638 ... 20.10.15
11.10.15	N.1. Hosp Valetta 157	B.H.O Admitted military dysyptery Valetta	Malta		0810 36/19 B.2156 8.11.15 11.46
9.10.15	H.S. Assaye	B.H.O Admitted Hospital Dysy "Anzac"			
29.11.15	4 S Brickle	B.H.O Embarked for England per "Franconia"	Malta		0810 391/5135 ... 26.11.15 ...
...	W.O. List ... 2nd ...	Admitted 2nd Birmingham War ...	England		0810 361/248 6.12.15
13.4.16	... Embarkation Office	Proceeded to Weymouth join B.E.F.	Weymouth	13/4/16	D7092 451
29.4.16	B.213	Returned to West	France	25.4.16	0810 409/690 A.C 224 8.8.16
28.16	N.C. Lyn 43rd	A.H. ... Resuscitated	Camps...		11.8.16 /0.9.16

(a) In the case of a man who has re-engaged for, or enlisted into section 11, Army Reserve, particulars of such re-engagement or enlistment will be entered. P.T.O
(b) e.c., Signaller, Shoeing, Smith, etc., etc., also special qualifications in technical Corps duties.

Turkish bullets and bombs weren't the only killers for the Anzacs. Tasman hadn't been on Gallipoli long when he was struck down by 'Gallipoli Gallop', the name given to body-and-soul-breaking bouts of dysentery. (National Archives of Australia)

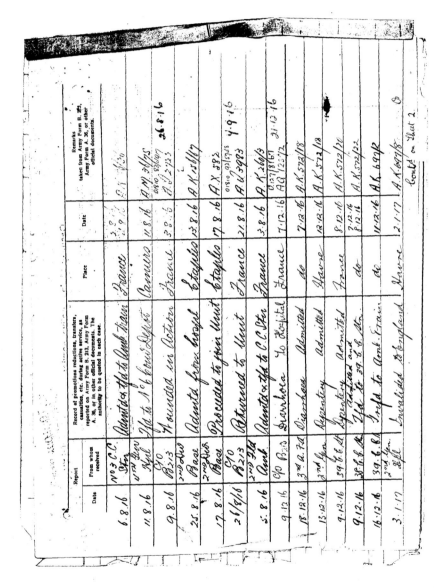

Tasman was not long out of the hospital when he was wounded in action for the first time. (National Archives of Australia)

2431.—Wt490/1535.—2,000,000—J. J. K. & Co., Ltd.—Forms B. 103/1.

Army Form B. 103.

Regtl. No.

1146

Sheet 2.

Casualty Form—Active Service.

Regiment or Corps "D" Coy. 26th Battalion. Name Millington Tasman

Rank Private

Regimental No. 1146

Terms of Service (a) War + 4 months Service reckons from (a) 23.4.15

Enlisted (a) 23.4.15

Date of promotion to present rank

Date of appointment to lance rank

Re-engaged

Extended

Numerical position on roll of N.C.Os.

Qualification (ö)

Report		Record of promotions, reductions, transfers, casualties, etc., during active service, as reported on Army Form B. 213, Army Form A. 36, or in other official documents. The authority to be quoted in each case.	Place	Date	Remarks Taken from Army Form B. 213, Army Form A. 36, or other official documents.
Date	From whom received				
2.1.17	H.S. "Carisbrook Castle"	Dysentery Embarked for England.	Havre	2.1.17	DO.7/1499. AK699/18 29.1.17 ✓
3.1.17	66 Hospital	Adm 2nd to 3.H. Hospital	Brighton	3.1.17	QO6/1002 27/1/17 ✓
7.2.17	06 Hospital	Adm 3rd Aux Hospital trans from 2nd to 3.H.	Dartford	7.2.17	
26.3.17	66 Hospital	Discharged from 3rd Aux Hosp. for furlo 26.3.17 to 10.4.17	Dartford		✓
		& report to Trg Dept. Perham Dns			
16.4.17	A.I.F.No.1878	March to Camp: Hyde PD England	Perham Downs England	13/4/17 2R 184 Q. 13.2/3.	
18.4.14	do.	Mr. in from 4½ Q.G. Westfield Vicia	do	11.4.17 2R 1878. 13.2.13.	

(a) In the case of a man who has re-engaged for, or enlisted into Section D, Army Reserve, particulars of such re-engagement or enlistment will be entered.
(ö) e.g., Signaller, Shooting Smith, etc., etc., also special qualifications in technical Corps duties.

[P.T.O.

Chronic dysentery almost killed Tasman Millington, and he was to suffer the effects for many years after the war. (National Archives of Australia)

Report Date	Report From whom received	Record of promotions, reductions, transfers, casualties, etc., during active service, as reported on Army Form B. 213, Army Form A. 36, or in other official documents. The authority to be quoted in each case.	Place	Date	Remarks taken from Army Form B. 213, Army Form A. 36, or other official documents.
15·4·17	AJD Depot Perham Down	Pn/S from No.1 Com Depot	Perham Downs	12·4·17	L.R. 1768 32/E 3526 16·5·17
22·5·17	12 Infantry Troops Depot	Proceeding ahead, ex Perham Down	Southampton	22·5·17	LX·3111 x 34·3944 2·6·17
23·5·17	2 Div Base		France	23·5·17	x 34·3944
11·6·17	"		"	11·6·17	64·9
16·6·17	10·21 Bn		France	12·6·17	D.O.37/3944 26·6·14 B·213 B·21/311
19·1·18	"	Proceeded on leave to Paris	Belgium	13·1·18	B·213 B·21/55
26·1·18	"	Rejoined x	"	26·1·18	" B·21/56
2·3·18	"	Proceeded on English Leave	"	28·2·18	" B·21/64
23·3·18	"	Rejoined from English Leave	"	10·3·18	" B·21/112
14·9·18	"	Ob	France	31·8·18	P.O.207/3944·WP 23·9·18 B·33 B·21/84
1·9·18	15 Aug FA	SW Hand R Adm to No.8	"	31·8·18	AK 3044/17
11·9·18	61 C.C.S.	ann 94.0.AT	"	1·9·18	/5
1·9·18	6 Gen	adm	"	1·9·18	AK 3099/10
6·9·18	"	to England	"	6·9·18	"
8·9·18	Bath Aux Hy	adm JSMR Base	Base	4·9·18	69 RL2826·AR 300 373 565
6·11·18	3 Aux Hd Hy	Dis from ex Bath W.A.	Dartford	6·11·18	HR164. 93606
7·12·18		Dis 6·12·18 granted leave o/c Repl 6 to 2 C.D. Weymouth 20·12·18	"	6·12·18 20·12·18	17/134 6·02·J.

Tasman was shot again in France. He remarked to Pasha Ismail once that he was glad he'd been shot in France rather than Gallipoli, 'as the medicinal qualities of French Cognac are far better when offered by a lovely young nurse'. (National Archives of Australia)

Army Form B 103.

Casualty Form—Active Service.

Regimental Number. 1146.

Rank. Pte. Regiment or Corps.

Surname. MILLINGTON. Christian Name. Tasman

Religion. .... Age on Enlistment. .... years. .... months

Enlisted (a). .... Terms of Service (a). .... Service reckons from (a). ....

Date of promotion to present rank. .... Date of appointment to lance rank. ....

Re-engaged { .... { Qualification (b). ....

Extended { .... { .... or Corps Trade and rate. ....

Signature of Officer. ....

Occupation. ....

Report					
Date	From whom received	Record of promotions, reductions, transfers, casualties, &c., during active service, as reported in Army Form B.213, Army Form A. 36, or on other official documents. The authority to be quoted in each case.	Place of Casualty	Date of Casualty	Remarks Taken from Army Form B.213, Army Form A.36, or other official documents
		Embarked			
		Disembarked			
31·12·18	HIF Depo	Ph granted extension of return leave to 2·1·19	London	2·1·19	LX 1025
21·12·18	OC troops	Ple Due to report that date	London	20·12·18	LX 750
		20·12·18. who on instructed to report to 63 AIF for outfit at the age			
19·12·18	"	Ple Due to rept Weymouth			
		30·12·18 Leave extended 16·2·12·18	"	20·12·18	LX 750
30·12·18	"	Ple Leave expires 27·12·18 has been granted extension until	"	30·12·18	LX 928
		20·01·18 ex Weymouth			
3·1·19	B. 102	Ple M/Cross AIF Depot	Weymouth	2·1·19	LE 059

(a) In the case of a man who has re-engaged for, or enlisted into Section D, Army Reserve, particulars of such re-engagement or enlistment will be entered

(b) Signaller, Shoeing Smith, &c.

(2) Regtl. No. 12·1·0.

Months 1

W 8495 4N2732 20000 9/17 (2483) C. V. & J., Ltd., Form B/103 E/1887. **P.T.O.**

W 8495 4N2732 20000 9/17 (2483) C. V. & J., Ltd., Form B/103 E/1887.

Private 1146 Millington had already been recruited by MI6, and extensions of leave were being granted to allow for some basic training. (National Archives of Australia)

When MI6 decided they wanted a man out in the Dardanelles to 'keep an eye on the old enemy … and anything else of interest', they arranged for Millington to attend the British School of Telegraphy before his official discharge. (National Archives of Australia)

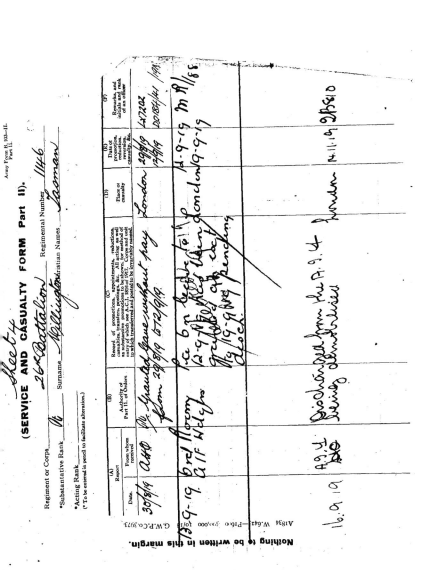

AUSTRALIAN IMPERIAL FORCE.

Proceedings on Discharge.

No. 1146   Army Rank   Pte.

Name   MILLINGTON.Tasman.

(The name must agree strictly with that on enlistment, unless changed subsequently by authority.)

Corps   26th Battalion,

Battalion, Battery, Company, Depot, &c.   Australian Imperial Force.

Date of Discharge   14.11.19.   Place of Discharge   London.England.

1.   *Description at time of discharge.*

Age   23   years   3.   months   Descriptive marks·

Height   5.   feet $7\frac{1}{2}$ inches

Chest measurement { girth when fully expanded   34   ins.

{ range of expansion   3   ins.   4 Vacc.Lt.Arm.

Complexion   Fair.   Scar Lt.Shin.

Eyes   Blue.   B.W.Rt.Forearm.

Hair   Medium.

Trade   WirelessOperator.

Intended place residence { Imperial War Graves Comn:
(To be given as fully as practicable)   Chahak.
       TURKEY.

†The measurements and description should be carefully taken on the day the man leaves his unit, but in the case of men sent home from abroad for discharge, the age and intended place of residence should be left blank to be filled in by the Officer, who confirms the discharge at home.)

2. The above-named man is discharged in consequence of **being Demobilised with effect from 14.11.19.**

(The cause of discharge must be worded as prescribed in the King's Regulations and be identical with that on the discharge certificate. If discharged by superior authority, the No. and date of the letter to be quoted.)

3.   *Statement of service in Australian Imperial Force.*   Medals and Decorations.

Service towards completion of engagement   4   years   206   days   1914-15. Star

Service abroad   „   „   4   years   139   days   British War Medal

Total   4   years   206   days   Victory Medal

4.   *Certificate to be signed by the soldier on discharge.*

I hereby acknowledge that I have received all my pay and allowances (including clothing allowance), and all just demands up to the present date, subject to the reservations of the claims noted on the 2nd page.

(Place) London.England.   *T. millington*   (Signature of Soldier.)

(Date) 15.9.19.   (Signature of Witness.)

(When a soldier is absent through illness or any other cause, and it is not desirable to forward these proceedings to him for signature, a manuscript copy should be sent for the man to sign, and when returned should be attached here.)

At just 23 years of age Tasman had been shot twice. One bullet tore away a favourite tattoo on his forearm, which for the rest of his life he said was the greatest loss of the Great War. (National Archives of Australia)

Members of the Australian Historical Mission at Hill 60 in
Gallipoli, 22 February 1919. (Commonwealth War Graves,
London)

Cemeteries both large and small grew up wherever fighting
had taken place. (Commonwealth War Graves, London)

Above and top right: The 'Rope-way', which was built by the War Graves Commission to carry stone from the quarry to the cemeteries. The rugged approaches to almost all of the Gallipoli cemeteries and the great weight of the stone slabs prevented trucks or even carts from being used. Cemeteries were built over the battlefields and, for the most part, soldiers were buried where they fell. (Commonwealth War Graves, London)

A Turkish stonemason splits and prepares stone for grave markers and monuments at Gallipoli, under the supervision of an officer of the Imperial War Graves Commission. (Commonwealth War Graves, London)

A cemetery under construction. The crosses indicate soldiers who could be identified. Markers without a cross are all 'A Soldier of the Great War', names unknown. Tasman Millington made every effort to identify the fallen and insisted that every unearthing and burial of remains be treated with great respect. (Commonwealth War Graves, London)

A photograph published in Reveille, 1934. The caption reads:
'Tasman Millington, 26th Bn, AIF and now in charge of the work of the Imperial Graves Commission at Gallipoli, is seen here at Anzac Beach – on the 20th anniversary of the Landing – scattering ashes secured from the burning of thousands upon thousands of ribbons which were attached to floral tributes at Sydney Cenotaph. The urn in which the ashes were sent to Gallipoli will be returned to Sydney with some soil from the battlefield of Lone Pine. For the consummation of this ceremony we are indebted to Col. C.E. Hughes ex AIF, who is the representative of the Imperial War Graves Commission in the East, with headquarters at Cairo.'

was there to take them down to the boat where they'd be met by Tasman. The two men had gone with him and when they reached the moorings Ismail leapt aboard the *Mary* and produced the sub-machine gun he'd planted there the night before. The Nazi had pulled a handgun from his coat pocket and Ismail fired a burst straight into his chest.

Tasman listened to the story as Gino poured more coffee. 'What about the captain here?' he asked.

Ismail leant forward on the kitchen table. 'I was ready to finish him off too – but he surprised me, Millington.'

'What do you mean, he surprised you?'

'The Italian, he surrendered!'

Gino interrupted. 'I do not like the war, I do not like the German. I will tell you everything you want to know. Do you have any sweet cake, Colonel?'

Tasman decided that it was going to be a very long war.

London asked Tasman to repeat the message. He had a what? Tasman repeated the message. He was then informed that he was in no position to have a POW! They'd have to get orders from higher up for this one, London said. They'd get back to him in the next transmission.

'Millington, Millington, the Italian is gone!' Ismail sounded in a huge panic.

Tasman covered up the radio and put the flooring back in place before racing out to Ismail. They got ready to go after the Italian but at that moment Gino came in the back door carrying two large suitcases. He'd been to the hotel to pay the bill and collect both his and the dead German's belongings.

Ismail was so pleased to see the Italian that he rushed to the door to help him in with the luggage, while Tasman gave a sigh of relief that his one and only POW hadn't bolted.

Captain di Steffano now retired from the war and the world of Intelligence work, handing over the case containing the radio transmitter and a pouch holding not only the black notebook the German had hidden under his bed but also various other papers and documents. Tasman scanned these briefly. They were mostly written in German, which prompted him to ask Ismail where he'd disposed of the dead Nazi.

'There was great confusion ... not enough time, Millington. The body is in the boat at the waterfront.'

Tasman was speechless, wondering what else could happen.

They had to get rid of the German's body before it was discovered by one of the Commission workers or an inquisitive soldier, but they couldn't just leave their POW to roam around the house on his own. Gino would have to come with them to the boat. Tasman found him some work clothes that he hoped would allow the captain to pass as a War Graves worker. The Italian agreed not to open his mouth if they met anyone.

Tasman wasn't sad to see the body slip over the side when they reached the open sea off Seddulbahir. They had weighted the canvas-shrouded corpse with a spare anchor and a length of chain. Gino indicated that he'd like to say a few words for his former comrade. Tasman nodded.

'Thank you, Colonel,' said Gino as he went to the stern of the boat. 'Holy Mother, this is the foul body of an evil Nazi I have been cursed to help. Now he lies dead and rotting in the sea. It is a good thing; send him to hell. Amen.'

The few words weren't exactly what Tasman had been expecting, and Ismail hurriedly turned away, shaking with laughter.

Back in Chanak the captain eventually admitted that he was an agent of the Servizio Informazione Militaire, a reluctant spy who'd been assigned to work with the German Abwehr. The German agent, who he knew only as Frick, and he had come to Chanak as Dutch merchant seamen, with orders to make detailed observations of Chanak itself, the Turkish military and its strength in the Dardanelles, and safe routes for Nazi agents going into Greece. They were also to pay special attention to Tasman Millington and his staff at the Imperial War Graves Commission, as well as their boats and other sea craft that could be useful to agents if needed. The German, Frick, had been making daily radio reports, most of the information unknown to Gino as the Nazi agent had considered the Italian to be inferior and unworthy of intelligence sharing.

'There is one other thing, Colonel,' said Gino. 'I do know that Frick was intending to kill you soon. He was waiting for the right time and place.'

Tasman now worried about how much the Nazi had known and what he had reported to his masters.

NINE

Around the middle of March 1941 London ordered Tasman to take the MTB out of Turkish waters and into the Aegean where, at a designated time and position, he would be met by an RAF Sunderland flying boat. Tasman and a man brought by the plane were then to return to Suvla Cove and make their way back to Chanak to await further orders. The operation was clearly of the highest importance – sending a Sunderland so far was a considerable risk.

Just before midnight three days later Tasman, Ismail and Joseph slipped the mooring lines and quietly guided the MTB out of the small inlet, opening the throttle wide only when they were twenty minutes clear of the coast. Tasman thought of

John Smith, who they'd taken to Greece along the same route, and wondered if he was all right or even still alive. One and a half hours out of Suvla, Tasman shut off the engines and loaded a flare into a Very pistol, then sat down to listen for the approach of the flying boat. Joseph brought hot coffee laced heavily with rum; Ismail said he'd be a very sad Russian when the rum finally ran out. The time came and passed with no sign of the Sunderland. No one said anything when another hour went by. Ismail could sense Tasman's concern. But as he looked across at his friend, the night air was filled with a deep sound – the Sunderland, flying low and watching for a signal.

The bright flare that Tasman sent high in the sky brought an almost immediate response. Two quick flashes of white light came from the nose of the Sunderland as it banked sharply and flew right over the MTB. A few minutes passed while the massive flying boat landed on the calm sea, turned around and steered towards them. When it stopped, Tasman idled the MTB up to a hatch in the side of the plane. It was now open and revealed a dull red glow outlining the figures of two men. Ismail stood at the MTB's bow, ready to help their passenger aboard, while Joseph held a boat hook with the idea that it might be needed. The transfer took place very quickly. Ismail reached down, the man gripped his wrist firmly and swung himself aboard, clutching a small suitcase. There was a wave from the other man, who stood in the plane's hatchway as Tasman eased the boat well away from the Sunderland. Then the powerful Pegasus engines lifted the flying boat forward, taking it across the water and up into the darkness of the sky.

Tasman headed the MTB toward Suvla, running at full speed. The passenger introduced himself as Major John Drakopoulos. His first name seemed right, but the Greek surname didn't really fit his looks. His appearance was more North European, at least to Tasman's eyes.

London now instructed Tasman to leave for Istanbul as soon as possible and to report to the British diplomatic mission. An Intelligence officer would meet him there. The whole thing was to be done quite openly in his capacity as Imperial War Graves representative. The Commission controlled three cemeteries in Istanbul, so the reason for going there wouldn't be questioned and in his official role Tasman had made inspection trips to the city a number of times before.

Ismail offered to accompany Tasman but there was the problem of Major Drakopoulos, the Special Operations Executive (SOE) agent. Ismail would have to stay behind and mind the shop. The mystery SOE man was awaiting his own orders, and if London took as long as they usually did then the safest thing to do with him was to put him over on the Peninsula in the care of one of the work parties, as Tasman had already done with Gino, the POW.

At the Embassy Major Millington was given a quick education on the politics of the war and the place Turkey had in it. The Intelligence officer suggested that the Turks mightn't be as neutral as they claimed. The Germans had their people everywhere, and by 'their people' the officer meant spies and agents, members of the Abwehr, the SS and the Gestapo. They were all very active in Turkey. Germany needed to trade with the Turks for chromium, and more importantly they were seeking assurance of neutrality in order to secure the southern flank of the Soviet Union. They'd stop at nothing to get it.

The Germans were bringing pressure on Turkey to close the Dardanelles to the Allies' warships, but Turkey had refused to do so. Passage through the strait was guaranteed by the International Montross Convention and, regardless of what threats Germany made, the heavyweight nations weren't going to allow Turkey to close it. So for the moment at least the Black Sea wasn't shut off from the rest of the world.

Tasman was now seeing a far bigger picture than he had before. Turkey was a hotbed of spying and underhand dealings between ally and enemy, with high stakes for all involved, including the strong possibility of Germany taking by force anything the Turks wouldn't give them. But Tasman hadn't been brought to Istanbul for a lesson in world politics; he was there to be briefed on his own role in what was expected to happen shortly in Greece. The Italians' blunder in not taking Greece meant almost certain intervention by Germany and when it came, he was told, it would be swift and exact.

Haidar Pasha Cemetery lies in a suburb of Istanbul at the site of the Crimean War graves. The hospital building beside it was operated by Florence Nightingale and her nurses during that war; it was only because of her insistence that the British Government persuaded the Turks to donate the land to be used for cemeteries. The graves of the Great War numbered 414. Some of the men in them had died of their wounds, some as prisoners of war; and others who'd been part of the postwar occupying force had been struck down by the influenza epidemic of

1918–19. Tasman inspected the three areas under the care of the Commission before returning to Chanak.

Ismail had news for him there and it wasn't good. Major Drakopoulos had received orders by radio the previous day. London had orders for Tasman as well. 'I wish it was just an April Fool's joke,' said Tasman when the Greek major confirmed the orders. Drakopoulos was to go to Greece and Tasman was not only to take him there but take him right into the lion's mouth just ahead of the expected invasion by the Germans.

The stage was set. In a few days' time they'd make the run from Suvla Cove to Salonika, a distance of about 800 kilometres there and back. Fuel, a lot of it, would need to be carried on the deck of the MTB. Ismail left Chanak for the trek to Suvla early the next morning to help Joseph prepare the boat. On this trip they'd need plenty of weapons and ammunition and Ismail had said it would be ready when the two majors arrived. Meanwhile, the usual daily radio calls with London rang alarm bells. 'Don't wait, act now without delay. Don't wait, act now without delay.' On 4 April, with Germany poised to make its move, Tasman and the Greek major crossed the narrows on their way to Suvla.

At the camp, while Ismail finished cleaning and oiling the weapons, Drakopolous put on the old civilian clothes he'd brought in his small suitcase. He looked thoroughly ordinary and Tasman now knew for certain that, whatever the assignment was, the major was going into great danger.

They got away very early in the morning, Drakopoulos gazing calmly at the lightening sky as the MTB eased out of the cove and headed for Salonika.

The Germans' move on Greece, the culmination of their overrunning of the Balkans, took place in the three weeks following 6 April 1941. Salonika would be in the thick of it when the German 12th Army thrust southwards from Bulgaria into Thrace and mechanised columns advanced on the harbour city through Macedonia. The Greek units in Thrace and southern Albania – together forming the bulk of the Greek Army – would find themselves immobilised. And a small British force that had landed at Salonika earlier would be no match for the Huns.

Tasman slowed the engines as they sighted Salonika and only then did Major Drakopoulos, who stood next to him at the wheel, say something of a personal nature. Looking straight ahead, he said: 'Home!' It was enough.

There were many fishing boats in the wide harbour, which made it relatively easy to simply put Drakopoulos ashore at the main wharf. With nothing more than his old suitcase, he jumped ashore and was gone in less time than it took Tasman to reverse the camouflaged MTB and move away. The job was done, no alarm had been raised, but a lengthy coastline had to be traversed before they reached the open Aegean. As the boat cut through the water it occurred to Tasman that he'd probably never see Drakopoulos again.

There was still a stretch of coast to put behind them when Ismail saw the Messerschmitt. Tasman slowed the engines to prevent the wake giving away the true identity of their pseudo-trawler. The aircraft was astern of the MTB and approached fast, flying right over the boat, then climbed high and began a steep turn. Tasman called to Joseph to start waving at the pilot when he flew over them again. As Ismail came up from below with two machine guns the plane raced back, buzzing them for the second time – and now there was no mistaking the markings of the Luftwaffe as the aircraft once more climbed high and began another sweep. Ismail quickly set up a Bren gun near the stern and gave it over to Joseph, then took a Vickers gun forward. Tasman searched the shoreline for cover that wasn't there.

The first burst of cannon fire from the Messerschmitt fell short, but the second found enough of the small mast to bring it crashing down in a rain of splinters. Ismail emptied half a belt of ammunition at the fighter to no avail and it was clear that the next pass was going to be hot. As the pilot turned in the distance, Tasman rapidly took stock of the damage and ordered Joseph to cut the petrol drums loose and push them over the side. The trio had been extremely lucky that the drums hadn't been hit, which would have turned the whole boat into a fountain of fire.

The aircraft dived steep and low, its wing guns erupting in a hail of rounds which first hit the water and then the boat, below and above deck. Ismail and Joseph worked feverishly at their own guns as the Messerschmitt flew over the MTB in a blur of shells and debris thrown up in every direction. All guns suddenly stopped, but ominous detonations continued in the boat. Smoke billowed from the main hatchway and flames were licking up through a forward air vent. The MTB was in bad shape and on fire. Below, exploding shells were ripping into the cabin walls. In an extraordinary act of desperation Tasman launched himself down the companionway and, grabbing a blanket, began beating out the fire. Ismail dropped through the forward hatch and joined him. Miraculously, they survived. They emerged from the cabin coughing and choking and half expecting to see the German fighter on another run, and Joseph fighting the boat.

Tasman looked at the stern and saw that the afterdeck had turned red. It was Joseph's blood. They ran over to the Russian, the deck slippery under their feet. The body had been torn apart by the German's cannon fire, leaving it with little resemblance to a whole human being. Joseph had clearly stood his ground behind the red-hot barrel of the machine gun and had died still firing it.

Ismail could say nothing. Tasman could only smell an old smell he remembered well, the haunting smell of blood.

The fighter plane had disappeared. Near the boat there was a fuel drum floating in the water. It might be enough to get them back to Suvla if the MTB held together and the gods of ancient Greece permitted. With a boat hook and rope Tasman and Ismail hauled the drum aboard.

The boat had suffered a good deal. The holes below the waterline weren't large but would allow the sea to flood in, and constant pumping would be necessary. Tasman inspected the engine room, finding only superficial damage to the main parts. The batteries had been hit and were leaking, but when he started the engines they fired up.

Getting underway, Tasman turned to the afterdeck to see Ismail with a sheet of canvas laid out; he was scooping up Joseph's shattered body, the flesh and bone cradled in his bare hands as he placed the fragments carefully on the shroud and finally covered them up. By night-time they were safely away from the coast, the pumps working overtime. The boat was afloat but only just.

Ismail stood beside Tasman as the Australian began to speak quietly. 'I think the bloke's name was Bill. I don't know if I ever knew his surname, he was just Bill. He was a good bloke, always gave me a fag when he came into the trench. I remember now, he was a water carrier. Good bloke!' Tasman said nothing for a moment. 'A bloody big shell came over one day and lobbed right into a trench where Bill was. When we went over to have a look there was nothing to see except for red mud – only red mud!'

Just then the engines coughed, shuddered and died completely. The forward movement of the MTB slowed and a small wave caught up with the boat as it came to rest. Tasman lifted the engine room hatch and saw that the compartment was flooded. Ismail looked to the heavens, then climbed into the oily muck and began passing buckets of water up to Tasman, who emptied them over the side. It took some time but the water level slowly dropped.

Their situation was now extremely serious. The engines needed drying out and there was probably seawater in the fuel lines, the hull had more holes in it than Swiss cheese, and they were slowly drifting north into the arms of the German Army. Tasman thought that things couldn't get any worse until Ismail said: 'Millington, here is your tobacco pouch – it was floating in the bilge!' The motors being out of commission meant there were no pumps to keep the sea at bay, so Ismail went on with bucket duty while Tasman worked frantically to get the engines running, and with the damaged batteries they'd have to start first time. Four hours passed before the fuel lines had been cleared and reprimed and the electrical leads dried out. Tasman readied each motor with the crank handle, switched the batteries to the on position and pressed the starter. The port side engine turned over slowly a few times then suddenly spluttered into life, followed by the other engine a few seconds later. They had power again, and were going to get home.

At Suvla Cove, with the bow of the MTB pressed into the beach, Tasman stood waist-deep in the water as Ismail lowered the canvas wrap containing Joseph's remains over the side and into his arms. Then he waded back to the beach and laid the bundle down gently. The dry and craggy ground of Suvla would be the Russian's resting place.

When Tasman tapped the final sod of earth down on the grave Ismail stepped forward with a water bottle filled with rum he'd taken from Joseph's barrel. Ismail poured a little of it over the soil, then took a drink himself before handing it to Tasman, who also drank. Words weren't necessary.

The two men agreed that the MTB could not be repaired without help and additional materials which they didn't have at Suvla. The Russian workers would be needed again. The pair returned to Chanak, where the radio told Tasman just how close they'd come to being in the front line. Germany had invaded Greece with a vengeance. A Panzer corps had swept down from Yugoslavia through the Monastir Gap, the British had deployed 75 000 troops into the mountains around Mt Olympus, and Salonika had fallen. 'God help John Drakopoulos,' Tasman thought, as he began to make his report to London. The news of the invasion created another worry. The Germans had spread their forces in Thrace as far east as Alexandroupolis, some 75 kilometres from the MTB at Suvla. The Luftwaffe had every chance of discovering it there.

'Millington, there is a problem!' Ismail had the knack of bearing bad news. 'There are more of the Dutch seamen, German agents, here in Chanak – at the hotel. They ask about their comrades, Millington!' Tasman waited for Ismail to offer to kill them and was surprised when he didn't. 'There is one other problem, Millington. The Italian, Gino, has gone out to meet them on the Lapseki road. He cannot be trusted, we must go after him now.'

Ismail's rattly old truck hadn't been driven so fast in its entire life. The wooden tray threatened to jump free of the chassis as Ismail veered from one side of the road to the other ignoring potholes the size of tractor tyres and sliding into bends sideways. Tasman hung on to the door with one hand and the seat springs with the other. Half an hour down the road they saw Gino on foot, walking back toward Chanak. Ismail stood on the brakes and some distance past Gino the truck decided to come to a stop.

Gino came up, happy to see them. Ismail sided with caution and kept his hand on the automatic pistol beside him while Tasman got out. 'Hello, Colonel,' said Gino. 'I have taken care of everything. The German dogs are dead!'

Understandably, the 'colonel' was having difficulty following this plot. 'What do you mean, Captain … "taken care of everything"?'

Gino snapped to attention, gave Tasman a salute and said: 'There were two new agents. They were known to me, Colonel. They would have made big trouble – mostly for me. I told them I will meet with them and make my report. They came. I shot them both, the pigs.'

Tasman leant on the mudguard of the truck and looked up at Ismail, who had nothing to say.

'Also, Colonel – here is the gun I borrowed from your house. It is very good, very accurate. I am pleased to give it back to you, I am a prisoner of war. Thank you.'

Tasman didn't ask Gino anything more, just looked out the window as Ismail drove the truck back to Chanak, very slowly, the three of them sitting in the front.

The Russian workers listened intently as Tasman told them how Joseph had manned his machine gun and defended the MTB against the superior firepower of the German fighter plane. Many of them nodded their approval and showed pride that Joseph had died a Russian hero. Ismail gave Joseph credit for saving his and Tasman's life. The readiness of the Russians to help repair the MTB now went without saying: they would consider it a personal duty, a chance to honour Joseph's sacrifice. They would do more than make repairs to the boat, they'd turn it into a floating fortress to strike back at the Germans. They'd make it a deadly cobra with many heads ready to strike.

Tasman still had Commission work to do and the Third Reich wasn't going to stop him doing it. The war was passing by the Gallipoli Peninsula as if that hallowed place was too sacred ever to see another drop of blood fall to its soil. The madness of war raged nearby, but here there was only the change of seasons to show that time had passed at all. Across the Aegean the Panzer tanks killed the silence, while on Gallipoli the loudest noise you could hear was the wind shuffling among the grasses or the dull rustle of pine branches as they were caught in a momentary flurry. As Tasman moved around the gravesites he acknowledged that the world hadn't learned a thing; they were doing it all over again. The power-mad leaders and all their blind followers should be brought here to see the price of peace ... Gallipoli, the priceless earth of Gallipoli.

The work on the MTB had begun. One of the Russians had worked in a shipyard and took charge of the work party as the sad-looking vessel was all but stripped bare. Ismail obtained materials from 'one of his cousins'; Tasman said he didn't want to know the details, as day after day Ismail would turn up with all manner of things that had clearly been liberated from the Turkish military. The Russians used everything and wasted nothing that they could salvage from the wreckage of the boat. The former shipwright improvised a method of forming protective armour, made from old water tanks, to shield a large section of the superstructure. Holes were cut in the iron to make gun ports and short wooden posts banded with leather thongs were devised to hold the mounts of machine guns. Down below they constructed a heavy metal box to hold ammunition and stop it from exploding if the cabin caught fire again. The deck, hull and other damaged areas were slowly restored and reinforced where possible.

But the greatest feat the Russians performed was the transformation of the MTB's colour and appearance. The boat had looked like a local fishing craft from a distance but that had clearly not fooled the fighter pilot. With good reason to think that the Germans would now attack any boat, the genius of Russian thinking had come to the forefront. When Tasman later looked down at the pier from the top of the hill he stood agape. He could scarcely see the boat at all, even at that short distance. The Russians had methodically repainted the craft in shades of blue, green and dull grey-black, the colours of the Aegean on which it sailed. Ismail had been busy too, building a small box lined with rubber beside the helm. 'For your tobacco, Millington,' he said. 'It's hard to light when it's wet!' Even the Russians laughed, which was a rarity. Another of the Commission workers had been spending his nights by the campfire making a huge camouflage net to cover the entire MTB from the prying eyes of any German aircraft that might stray over Suvla. With Joseph's death in mind, they'd tried to think of everything.

TEN

Major Drakopoulos had been lucky to get out of Salonika just ahead of the Germans, and after a harrowing train journey south he reached Athens railway station on 7 April. The major had his orders, secret orders he was to carry out at all costs, and the task wasn't going to be easy with the Nazi juggernaut getting closer to Athens every day. British forces were falling southward to Athens as well. They'd held back the German advance for as long as possible but Hitler's henchmen remained unstoppable as villages and towns were smashed into submission.

The Grande Bretagne Hotel in Athens was the last word in old-world luxury and elegance and since 1940 had served as the British headquarters in

Greece, but by the end of April the British were standing ready to make a fast departure. There was no doubt in the major's mind that when the Germans did take the Greek capital they would set up their own headquarters in the hotel. Accordingly, he made it his first priority to obtain a job there.

The British now left, the Germans filed into Athens and as the major had predicted they quickly took over the Grande Bretagne Hotel.

Under the command of Standarten Fuehrer Gellermann, black-uniformed SS troops took up residence and it wasn't long before Gellermann ordered all staff of the Grande be investigated, from assistant managers to cleaners, with special attention to be paid to any newer staff, such as Drakopoulos. The background check on him was very revealing indeed. Gellermann was highly impressed. The new staff member had lived ten years in Germany, was a graduate of a German university and had even taken part in the early Hitler rallies.

One morning in May the hotel was swamped by German officers, mostly from the Luftwaffe. But a good many of them were commanders of parachute units, which told the Greek major that the German plans included a drop from the sky. But where? The

Germans had options of Malta, Iraq or Crete. British Intelligence needed to know which, as far in advance as possible. Drakopoulos watched and listened. Then one day a careless German officer left behind a notepad. The cover page was torn away but the faint indentation under it was all that Drakopoulos needed. It spelt out the word Kreta, German for Crete, and had a date written in numerals – V 17 – so the place and date (17 May) were set.

Across the street from where the Gestapo held court and tortured, maimed, raped and murdered Greek civilians who got in their way, the Greek Underground and the SOE had set up a radio transmitter right under the noses of the Germans, and it was from there that a signal about the German plan to invade Crete was sent to a submarine which then relayed the message to London.

Tasman had informed London that the MTB was operational again, but had been told to wait. During his daily radio transmission some days later he was warned to be ready for orders within 24 hours. Ismail shrugged his shoulders when Tasman told him.

'Perhaps now we can make war on the Germans – if your people in London can ever decide, Millington.'

Tasman had no way of knowing it but the island of Crete had been suffering a daily onslaught by the Luftwaffe. British command in Crete was chaotic to say the least. Seven months of occupation had seen a new commander appointed every month. It was a recipe for disaster as more and more troops poured in from the Greek mainland after being driven into the sea by the German Army. The British Prime Minister, Winston Churchill, was all too aware that if Crete fell into the hands of Germany, Hitler would be able to launch massive attacks. Churchill needed not just a great commander of men but a commander of commanders to take overall charge of Crete and the coming invasion from the skies.

There was only one choice as far as Churchill was concerned – a New Zealander, Major General Bernard Freyberg, VC, DSO with two bars. The Kiwi was a legend and a hero in his own right. If Crete was to be held then Freyberg was the man for the job. He had been known to Churchill since World War I and the PM held him in the highest regard as a soldier and a personal friend. Freyberg took the command. His first observation was the same as Churchill's. Crete, if it fell into the hands of the Nazis, would give them the upper hand in North Africa, all of southern Europe and the East, as well as securing the vast oilfields of Romania to fuel the German machine. Crete must be held at any price, and the price was going to be high.

When Freyberg arrived he found that he had nothing to work with, no staff or aides, not even a wireless operator to assist him. He quickly appointed a Colonel Stewart to find him a staff, a whole headquarters staff, as soon as possible.

The Luftwaffe hounded the island and supply lines were being cut to the point where only a small percentage of supplies were getting through. Freyberg delegated areas of command to his senior officers and put his defence plan into action. Time, as far as Crete was concerned, was fast running out.

The King of Greece had fled to Crete and taken up residence at the Manos Villa at Pelikapina. The fact that the King was on the island was a constant concern for General Freyberg. The King was far from safe and in fact stood in the way of German ambitions. Freyberg asked him to leave while he still could and go to safety in Cairo. King George refused to go; Freyberg wasn't pleased. Within days the King decreed that all four Greek armies present on Crete were now under the command of the general. Again Freyberg wasn't too happy, but there was little he could do.

The Greeks, in total, numbered about 15000. Untrained and with scarce and old weapons, they looked as though they'd be of little use when the time came. General Freyberg had them posted to areas where he felt they'd survive better when the shooting started. The Luftwaffe was steadily increasing its daily attacks: the bombs fell while fighters strafed targets, buildings exploded and the people of Crete died. Bodies rotted and the death stench became commonplace all over the island. Every day the invasion grew closer. The harbour at Suda Bay was littered with the wreckage of vessels. The British warship HMS *York*, aground since being put out of action on 26 March by an Italian EMB, or explosive motor boat, offered pathetic testimony at the end of the bay.

The German Intelligence services had a great deal in common with their counterparts in Britain. They were experts in getting things wrong.

Lieutenant General Student, the commander of the Parachute Corps and the chief designer of the invasion plan, had assured Hitler of a swift victory in only a few days once his troops were on the ground. German Intelligence sources had reported to Student that there were less than 10000 British soldiers on Crete, but their best news was that among the Cretan people there were many Nazi sympathisers. The invaders could expect a warm welcome with very little resistance. The German general had been pleased to hear it.

Tasman was still awaiting orders. London's idea of 24 hours turned into a week before word came, and when it did it was as clear as mud. Millington was to take the MTB down to Bozburun, on the southwest corner of the Turkish coast, not far from Marmaris, and make contact with Colonel Keith Stewart, General Freyberg's chief of staff on Crete. He was to contact him by wireless, when further orders would be given. And the Turks were to be kept well out of it!

Tasman walked down to the Chanak waterfront, where he found Ismail working on the Commission boat with Gino.

'Millington, is there any news yet? Do we join in the war?'

Tasman was worried about the question being asked in front of the Italian captain, and was about to lead Ismail out of hearing range, when Gino said: 'It is all right, Colonel, Ismail has told me everything of your gunboat. It is very good, it will kill many of the filthy German pigs. I would like to volunteer myself, but I am a prisoner of war. For me the war is over, Colonel.'

Ismail averted his eyes as Tasman stared at him and said: 'You told the captain everything about the MTB did you, Ismail?'

'Millington, Gino can do no harm. He is your prisoner.'

Tasman looked at Gino, then turned back to Ismail. 'And if you go on telling everyone in Chanak then for us the war could be over sooner than you think!'

That afternoon, with the Italian captain absent, Tasman informed Ismail of London's orders. Ismail was very excited.

There still remained a small problem in that the MTB lacked one crewman since the loss of Joseph and, regardless of the Russian workers volunteering, Tasman was reluctant to use any of them. Their loyalty and fierce hatred of the Germans were a good thing, but their sea skills were all but nil and there was no time left to correct that even if Tasman wanted to. He and Ismail would have to handle the MTB alone, at least until he could think of something.

Among the final preparations, excuses had to be dreamt up not only for Tasman's absence but also for Ismail's. His wife and family were bound to ask many questions about where and why and how long he'd be gone, questions hard to answer except with a lie or at least an omission of facts.

There were moments when Ismail would ask himself why he was even involved. It wasn't as if

Turkey was at war with Germany or under immediate threat of attack. Ismail came to the conclusion that the twenty years or so he'd spent working with Tasman Millington had made him lose his mind. There'd been times when Millington had frustrated him so much that it had brought on a throbbing headache. Millington was the stubbornest man he'd ever known and yet there'd been times when he'd seen a man with the biggest heart in the world. Millington laughed a lot, he had that strange sense of humour that only Australian men seemed to have. His devotion to duty in regard to the war graves had earned him the highest respect from Ismail's fellow Turks. Millington was a friend.

Across the Aegean, in mainland Greece, the Germans were ready. Long before dawn the Luftwaffe's heavy bombers, Stuka dive-bombers and fighters took off ahead of the transports and gliders to mass bomb Crete ahead of the parachute invasion. The Luftwaffe had mustered 650 aircraft to ensure a blanket blitz of the island. Victory was certain, the Germans knew, and Crete would be secured in a matter of days. It was 20 May 1941.

Tasman nosed the bow of the MTB southward, the coolness of the mid-evening hour enjoyable as the boat cleared Cape Helles and moved down the coast well inside Turkish waters. The deck carried every last drop of fuel they'd had left at Suvla Cove; not knowing when more would become available they'd taken it all. Ismail took the precaution of loading up the machine guns and bringing small arms up to the bridge area, even though the Germans were still a long way away. Ahead there were more urgent dangers, and just as lethal. Running at speed close inshore along the rugged coast needed two pairs of eyes on constant watch for rocks and Turkish fishing craft. Many of the latter carried nothing but a small fuel lamp.

'Millington, please watch all before the bow. I will bring coffee.' Ismail was getting to be quite the first officer.

'Yes, sir,' said Tasman. 'Any further orders, sir?'

Ismail turned as he entered the hatchway and gave a broad grin.

The Luftwaffe bombers blackened the Cretan sky just after six in the morning. The island was hit again and again by waves of bombs falling to earth in huge payloads of destruction that the Germans hoped would cripple the armies, destroy the buildings, wreck the defences and break the people's spirit. And they were right on all accounts except one. The spirit of the Australians and New Zealanders, the British, the Greek soldiers and Cretans alike was still bright and alive when the dust settled and the iron rain stopped falling from the spring morning sky. The inextinguishable torch that all free people carry was now burning brighter, fanned by those who were sent to put it out.

The heavy bombers peeled away and were replaced by Stuka dive-bombers and Messerschmitt fighters which strafed anything in the pilots' sights. They came like swarms of metal-clad locusts devouring all before and beneath them. Suda Bay was cloaked in the smoke of burning ships, much of Crete was a vision of Hades.

Then the air attack began to slow and an hour into the assault it suddenly stopped. The skies over Crete filled with a kaleidoscope of colours as German paratroops descended in silken quiet from the hushed gliders high above. Ground fire came from anti-aircraft guns and small arms, taking a heavy toll on the floating invaders. German gliders carrying more troops were cut to pieces, bringing them crashing down and crushing their occupants. As other paratroops landed in their thousands, Allied soldiers and the people of Crete killed them in their hundreds wherever they found them, in any way they could – rifle and machine gun, scythe and pitchfork. Before the day ended the German invader would know he'd come to Crete, and would regret it.

The tiny village of Bozburun sat perched on the edge of the Turkish coast, the Aegean lapping its front door and rugged emptiness guarding its rear. The MTB would be safe here in the middle of nowhere, yet only 200 kilometres or so from Crete.

Tasman and Ismail had no idea that the bloody battle for the island had started until Tasman intercepted a wireless signal the night after they arrived at Bozburun. It wasn't difficult to guess what was happening behind the garbled sounds emitted by the radio. Tasman attempted to make contact with Colonel Stewart but they were still too far away; they'd need to get closer, which meant leaving the neutrality of Turkish waters.

They cleared Bozburun in the early morning darkness. Tasman asked Ismail to take the wheel while he went below, returning after a few moments and walking up to the short mast with a folded cloth in his hand. When Tasman took over the helm again Ismail saw that he had raised an Australian flag on the mast head. 'Wouldn't want to get us blown out of the water by our own blokes!' Tasman said. Ismail grinned.

After more fruitless attempts to raise Colonel Stewart at Creforce headquarters, Tasman decided to anchor at the small island of Saria at the northern tip of Karpathos, a little over 100 kilometres from the coast of Crete. They lay off Saria for several days listening to the war over the radio and trying to get on to Creforce. Then Tasman took the MTB to within 50 kilometres of Sitia, a town at the eastern end of Crete. Again they failed to contact Stewart. By sunrise Tasman had given up hope and was thinking of returning to Bozburun when they heard the drone of aircraft engines some distance away. The sky was clear and the planes were easily spotted flying low and slow: JU–52 transport planes in German markings, two of them and flying without escort.

Tasman and Ismail manned the machine guns. The Luftwaffe transports were well within range when

Ismail cut loose a volley of fire from the deck and almost immediately Tasman opened up as well. Both pilots banked steeply in a vain move to avoid the deadly fire. This only made their plight worse, as it exposed more of the wings and fuselage to the rounds being sent up from the boat. The shells ripped and tore at the sluggish planes, blasting away whole sections of frame and skin. The lead aircraft billowed smoke and the second JU–52 went into a slow spiralling descent, having lost most of its tail and rudder.

Ismail concentrated his fire on the lead plane and after a moment Tasman also brought his machine gun to bear, blowing away a wing. The aircraft burst into a ball of flame as it slipped from the skies into the Aegean. The other JU–52 crashlanded on the sea, smoking and smouldering in the boiling water. It was impossible to tell if there were any survivors but Tasman got the engines running and headed towards the plane.

Ismail looked at Tasman. 'Millington, even if there are men still alive, we can't take them on board.'

Tasman didn't answer. Ismail persisted.

Tasman snapped at him: 'If there are survivors, we will treat them as prisoners of war. There'll be no shooting prisoners, is that clear?'

Ismail nodded.

The lead plane had gone straight down; only flotsam remained on the surface. Reaching the other aircraft, Tasman could see two figures in the remnants of the cockpit. One was struggling to get free. Tasman moved the MTB alongside and called to Ismail to get a rope on the JU–52. As Ismail plunged over the side holding a rope, the plane began to settle in the water. Ismail kicked toward it, trying to reach something to tie the rope to. Tasman hung over the side of the boat and called to him to come back – it was getting dangerous. Ismail did so and Tasman helped him aboard. A few moments later the plane and the men in it were gone.

Tasman finally made contact with Colonel Stewart, who had only one order for him: 'Stay well away from Crete, Major. The bloody Germans are everywhere. There's nothing you can do here except get all your crew and yourself killed.'

Tasman looked at all his crew – Ismail – and smiled. He wondered what the colonel would say if he knew that they were within 50 kilometres of Sitia at that very moment. But Stewart was right – there was little they could do. Tasman started up the MTB and they returned to Bozburun, where they received orders to get themselves back to Chanak and wait.

ELEVEN

Crete was in fact going under, and on the night of 28 May 1941 the Allied forces began to be evacuated by the Royal Navy. The threat posed by the Luftwaffe was acute and while more than 16 000 men, including 2000 Greeks, were taken off, many thousands were not. The Germans demanded that those still on the island surrender, but a lot of them chose to fight on and to escape if and when they could.

Cretans fought alongside these Allied men and gave them aid in numerous ways. For this the Cretans paid a heavy price. Nazi execution squads roamed the villages and farmlands, pulling people out of their homes and shooting them, while others were held as hostages or used in German work gangs.

Strangely enough, Hitler didn't capitalise on his success in Crete – as Britain had expected him to do – by moving on Malta or Syria or Suez. Instead, on 22 June, he invaded Russia. Heavy Luftwaffe bombers attacked 66 Russian airfields and simultaneously a number of important cities, including Sevastopol and Odessa on the Black Sea. German army groups rolled in, one in the north, one in the south and one in the centre. Italy and Romania declared war against Russia; Hungary and Albania followed suit within days. The pattern of the war had changed altogether, and Turkey was now close to yet another centre of action.

In the midst of this turmoil to the north, Tasman had a surprise visitor at Chanak. It was John Smith, the British Intelligence man who Tasman had put ashore at Kimi on the other side of the Aegean some nine months before. He had with him two Australians of unstated occupation who had to get back to England. The pair were to be picked up by an RAF plane at an obscure airstrip near Bergama, about 150 kilometres to the south, in 48 hours' time. London had instructed Smith to get them there and then return to Chanak.

Tasman knew what was coming, and it did. Once again they made the trek to Suvla Cove; once again they headed down the Turkish coast. Ismail took Smith and the other two inland to the airstrip, saw the Australians off and returned with Smith to Tasman, who was waiting offshore in the MTB. Tasman was beginning to feel like a taxi driver.

Millington was aware that thousands of soldiers had been left on Crete, left to the merciless Hun. He also knew that they wouldn't give up without a fight. They'd been there now for some time and many would die there. Tasman thought it over and, in the absence of orders from London, sent a signal himself. The message was straightforward enough as far as he was concerned, but Smith, when he heard about it, called it outrageous. Tasman had told London that he was going on a fishing trip down south and had ended by saying: 'You never can tell what I might catch!' He'd closed down the radio before a response could be made.

'You do realise, Millington, that I can't possibly take part in some unauthorised operation that hasn't been organised by my people.' Smith sat down, irritated.

'Of course you can,' said Tasman blandly.

In the end, Smith agreed to go along with the plan.

The problem now was fuel. Their existing supplies were getting low. Tasman thought of Ismail's cousin, who had helped them in the past to acquire things that were simply not available. Three days later Ismail reported that the required petrol could be provided, but at a price — £2000 to be exact. Smith was shocked at the figure but agreed to put in a request to London on some pretext or other. When approval came through, he took himself off to Istanbul to collect the money.

A further difficulty was that, following Joseph's death, there was no suitably qualified crewman. Tasman had decided they'd have to do without one, as they had before. But such are the fortunes of war that this problem solved itself.

When they reached Suvla Cove to board the MTB for the run south, a group of Russian workers came up to them, wanting to volunteer for whatever mission they were on. Tasman had previously dismissed the idea of using the Russians — apart from Joseph — for this kind of work, but now it occurred to him that there might be another Joseph among them. He thanked the men for their offer and then said: 'But

I will need only one man. Which of you knows most about the boat's engines?'

The Russian workers' heads all turned to a man called Yuri. Tasman remembered that he had done some work on the MTB's engines and steering gear.

Yuri stepped forward and Tasman asked him if he wanted to act as the boat's engineer and, more to the point, whether he was aware that what had happened to Joseph could easily happen to him. The smile on Yuri's face was sufficient answer.

The Allied soldiers' means of getting off Crete were becoming less and less, as usable local boats were being destroyed by German patrols as soon as they discovered them. At the same time soldiers were escaping from the German prison compound and heading to the coast. Many were soon recaptured. The Germans began shipping their prisoners to Kokkinias Prison outside Athens, something that gave these Allied soldiers a chance to escape – which they often did, much to the annoyance of the master race. The Greek Underground had put in place a very efficient escape route using small fishing vessels to carry men to freedom in Alexandria.

John Smith had a sound working knowledge of the Greek Underground and he'd told Tasman some of the details, adding that he felt the Underground would be of little use to Tasman's plan unless the two of them set in place an escape route of their own from the Turkish side, which would then link up with the Greeks.

The MTB made a fast run down the coast to Bozburun where, on their earlier trip, they'd unloaded and hidden their spare barrels of fuel. Tasman spent long hours before dawn listening to radio chatter from Crete, and the decided lack of English being broadcast told him that the whole island was firmly in the hands of the enemy. Getting soldiers off would mean going ashore and finding them. Finding them, that is, while the Germans were looking for Tasman and his men as well.

Before their run across to Crete Tasman made one thing clear to Ismail, Smith and Yuri – that he and he alone would be going ashore to look for Allied troops while the others, under Ismail's direction, stayed on the MTB and kept it well out of sight. Smith had agreed before leaving Suvla to accept orders from Ismail on boat-handling matters.

Ismail was alarmed at Tasman's decision. 'Millington, you do not look like a Greek man, you do not look like a Turk. You will stand out brighter than the sun at noon time. It is I who should go on land and look for the soldiers.'

Smith had something to say about it as well. 'Will your German and Greek be good enough if required? I don't like to brag, but mine are near perfect. Certainly good enough to fool anyone. Suppose I go ashore when we get there, stretch my legs – that sort of thing. What do you say?'

Tasman said he was grateful to them but it had to be him. He would wear clothes that made him as inconspicuous as possible and carry his gun in an old sack.

The no man's land of sea stretched out wide before the bow of the MTB as it thumped its way over the chop toward Crete and the unknown. The first landing was to be at an isolated point on the coast not far from Sitia, where Tasman hoped to make contact with local Cretans. As the boat finally neared the shore in the starlight, he slipped over the side into a raft and paddled through the gentle waves, coming to rest between two rocky outcrops where he hid the raft. He made his way up the cliff, taking with him his 9mm Sten gun and extra ammunition. Ismail eased the MTB out to sea and took it round to the south coast, where Tasman thought it safest to be during daylight. Not that any of them considered their location safe – they were sitting right at the edge of German-occupied Crete. Tasman was due to return to the drop-off point at nine that night, along with any Allied men he'd come across. Ismail knew there was a long day of waiting ahead.

Tasman was relieved when, after hours of cautious exploration, he could see no sign of Germans anywhere near Sitia. Instead, he came across two villagers, an old man and a boy of perhaps 15 or 16, pushing a cart along a road. The boy saw Tasman emerge from behind a tree, cradling a sub-machine gun in his arms. Alerted by the boy, the old man stopped and threw his arms over his head as Tasman came closer. Suddenly the boy reached into the cart, picked up an MP38 machine pistol and aimed it at Tasman.

Raising his hands, Tasman called out: 'Australian, Australian!'

The result was immediate. The young Cretan lowered his gun and the old man broke into a wide smile, showing his few remaining teeth. Tasman awkwardly extended his hands in a gesture of friendship and the three of them moved the cart off the road and went to a clump of bushes where they were out of sight.

The lad spoke schoolboy English, allowing Tasman to find out that, while there were no Germans in the vicinity, patrols were very regular. Hearing this, Tasman pointed to the machine pistol.

'It is very good gun!' the boy said. 'The German, he has no more use for it – my grandfather cut him in the neck.' Apparently the grandfather guessed what the boy was saying: he reached across with a leathery old hand and patted the machine pistol before raising his fingers to his throat and drawing them slowly across from ear to ear. Tasman asked if they'd seen or heard of Australian or English soldiers in the area.

The boy said: 'There were men of New Zealand. They came but now they have gone.'

Tasman took out a map of the island that John Smith had prepared for him based on a military chart and his own recollections from a visit he'd made there before the war. The old man looked at it closely before pointing to a mountain area in the southwest of Crete, referred to on Smith's map as the White Mountains. He then said something to the boy, who also pointed to the White Mountains.

'Here. My grandfather says they will go here. Maybe men from Australia and England too.'

After getting crucial information about where the Germans were concentrated, Tasman thanked the two

Cretans for their help and headed back to the isolated pick-up point.

He was almost there when he spotted a four-man German patrol at the top of the cliff above the concealed raft. It was a blow, or would be if they stayed there. In another few hours Ismail would be back with the MTB and it would be heard and perhaps seen by the Germans. They seemed to be just resting by their small truck and having a smoke, but when nightfall came and they hadn't budged, Tasman decided to take things into his own hands. In the growing darkness he moved closer to their position and at eight o'clock, with only an hour to go until the MTB arrived, he rushed the Germans. They had no chance as his Sten gun spat at them.

Tasman stood there looking at the bodies, memories of other violent deaths returning once more. He knew that he'd have to clean up the mess – any sign of a killing would bring quick retribution to the local villagers. He removed the uniforms of two of the dead men and put them in his sack. Then he loaded the bodies into the patrol vehicle and, taking his gear, drove along the track looking for a point where the cliff fell sharply to the water. Finally he found a spot that seemed good enough. He threw the sack and his gun to the ground and jumped clear of the truck as it rolled toward the edge. He could only hope that when it hit the water it would sink out of sight.

Ismail came in on schedule and Tasman had been right about the possibility of someone hearing the engines and then seeing the outline of the MTB. The Germans could well have done some real damage as Ismail brought the boat in. When Tasman climbed on board, Ismail and Smith were very glad to see that he was still in one piece. As Yuri hauled the raft up on deck Ismail looked in Tasman's sack and pulled out the two German uniforms. He said: 'Millington, I see you have been hunting and brought back trophies!'

Then Smith chimed in. 'My God, Millington, Crete must be infested with giant moths. Just look at the size of these holes!'

Back in the relatively safe waters of Bozburun, Tasman put Yuri to work repairing the German uniforms, then tried to mollify Smith, who'd badly wanted to have a crack at Jerry too but hadn't been allowed. 'You'll get your chance, Smith, I promise you. There's plenty of them around.' He wasn't exaggerating. The

German invaders were firmly entrenched at Kastelli, Maleme, Suda Bay, Akrotiri and from Rethimnon to Iraklion. They were everywhere, and they were dug in for the long haul. The rugged and wild White Mountains, however, were likely to be a stronghold of sorts for possibly hundreds of New Zealand, Australian and English troops who'd escaped or evaded capture by their would-be Aryan masters. It was the place to which Tasman needed to go.

A day or so later Yuri appeared with the uniforms. He'd darned the 'moth holes' and had somehow managed to remove most of the dried blood. Even Smith thought the uniforms would pass muster. He tried on a jacket for size. 'Reasonable fit too, Millington,' he said. 'Had me in mind, did you?' Tasman was amused.

They studied the maps of Crete with care and settled on a landing place some little distance to the east of the fishing village of Sfakia, facing the Mediterranean on the south coast of the island. If they weren't discovered beforehand, Tasman told the others, he was confident that he could get ashore and make contact with members of the local Resistance, who would lead him to soldiers in hiding.

But Smith knew that this time Tasman wouldn't be able to go alone, and told him so. 'You have to be reasonable about this,' he said. 'You were lucky last time but this time you'll be rubbing shoulders with the Germans. You don't speak German, so when you're caught – and you will be caught – they're going to shoot you twice. Firstly for wearing a German uniform and being a spy, and then, just for the hell of it, for being so damned stupid and getting captured. And all because you're unable to speak Hitler's preferred language.'

Tasman rolled one of his ugly cigarettes and then lit it, cursing as the clumsily wetted paper disintegrated rapidly. 'You might be right,' he said.

Ismail was unusually quiet, feeling not for the first time that Smith was usurping him. Tasman turned to his friend. 'We need you to stay in charge of Yuri and the boat, Ismail. The whole operation will be a total failure if you're not there when you're needed. And do me a favour, keep the boat out of the hands of the Germans or none of us'll get home.'

Ismail looked disappointed but said nothing. He handed Tasman something wrapped tightly in a piece of cloth. 'What's this?' Tasman asked.

'Millington, I have made you some cigarettes. They are all nice and the same shape and size. If the Cretans see the ones you make they will lose confidence in you and perhaps join the enemy!' The gesture touched Tasman deeply.

In the evening he and Smith sat on the afterdeck talking about the war. The entire world had gone mad. Not only was Europe ablaze but now Asia and the Pacific were caught up in a deadly pattern of thrust and counter-thrust.

After a while the two men fell silent. Then Smith said tentatively: 'Looking at what's happening, I can't help wondering if there's some sort of plan behind it all.' This was not quite the Smith that Tasman knew, and he remained quiet. Smith went on: 'You know, at home in Kent I once had a remarkable conversation with the local minister. He said he believed that all the churches, all the religions, diminish God by claiming to speak for him and to know what he has in store for the world. The good Reverend, I remember, likened it to lifting a candle flame to the sunlight. How can a candle help you see the sun more clearly? How can any man or church pretend they know the plans of God? I think the Reverend was right – just look at all those crystal stars!'

The MTB slowed to a stop just off the coastline eastward of Sfakia. Ismail and Yuri lowered the raft over the side in the darkness, and Tasman and Smith climbed into it and rowed away. Ismail watched them go, then engaged the engines and took the boat out to sea. He had his orders from Tasman and was to return in two nights' time. Tasman had also made it clear that, if there was no sign of either Smith or him within a couple of hours of the rendezvous time, Yuri and Ismail were to take the MTB back to Bozburun, scuttle it and make their way to Chanak by whatever means they could. But Ismail knew that if necessary he would wait indefinitely for their return – and then explain to Millington that he'd gone a bit deaf.

Tasman and Smith hid the raft in a small sea cavern, lashing it to rocks to prevent it being washed away as the tide rose. They then took their equipment packs and weapons up the cliff to a small plateau, where they waited until the first pink streaks of dawn appeared.

The two men knew there would be a heavy concentration of Germans in Sfakia, but had agreed that the village gave them the best possible chance of making quick contact with the Resistance in that region. Dressed in their German uniforms, they walked off toward Sfakia. 'I hope the enemy are not too inquisitive,' Smith said. 'We both look about as German as Churchill does.'

In the morning light the village appeared calm. Cretans were going about their work, some of them mending nets on the seafront. As well, several work parties, guarded by Germans, were standing in the village square. The whitewashed stone houses were dwarfed by the high, white mountains behind them. The calm scene was deceptive. Neither Tasman nor Smith could have known it at the time but the small fishing village had seen a mass evacuation of Allied soldiers. Ships of the Royal Navy had boarded 3700 troops for transport to Alexandria and it was above Sfakian waters that General Freyberg, in a Sunderland flying boat, had had his last look at an island lost to the German victors.

Tasman decided they'd wait and watch for a while. Sooner or later a local villager would come along – the sooner the better. The work parties headed up the mountain road out of sight. Smith said: 'What say I wander down there and have a chat with the locals?' Tasman nodded. Smith went down to a group of women washing clothes at the water's edge. A conversation took place, ending with one of the women pointing to a house and Smith strolling off towards it.

After fifteen long minutes Tasman had shouldered his machine pistol and was walking toward the house, trying to look very German, when Smith came out of the doorway. Seeing Tasman, he quickly looked around and beckoned.

Inside, a short, stocky Cretan man stood up and seized Tasman's hand and shook it vigorously. 'Ya su! Bloody good, mate – Australian! Bloody good.' Obviously the man had come into contact with other Australians.

Smith explained what he'd been told by the villager, whose name was Nicholas. 'He says he will take us to a man tonight, a chap from a Greek regiment who's up in the mountains and causing a fair bit of bother for Jerry. He's up there with some Australians, some British fellows and a few others from New Zealand. Nicholas thinks there's about a dozen of them or maybe more.'

Tasman asked Smith to tell the man they were very pleased he could help them.

They could not remain in Sfakia. The Germans would return later in the day with the work parties and might get curious. Nicholas gave Smith some food to take with him and the three men agreed to meet at a specific point above the village after nightfall.

The Cretan turned up as promised and they headed up into the wilderness, the two agents stopping now and then to recover, much to Nicholas's amusement. After a couple of hours of hard slogging they reached the mouth of a cave hidden deep among twisted bushes.

The first to see them was a lookout, a Greek dressed in what remained of a proud uniform, still being proudly worn. He held a British Sten gun with its muzzle pointed straight at Tasman and Smith who stood there in the dim light, resplendent in their despised German uniforms.

Nicholas shouted out urgently, to prevent a possible bloodbath. Then he said in Greek, pointing at Tasman: 'This man is an Australian.' He added in English: 'A bloody good mate!'

Inside the deep cave a very Australian voice said: 'Well, bugger me. They're our blokes, dressed up like Adolf's nancy boys and nowhere to go.'

The Australian came out and shook hands first with Smith, who said: 'Good to see you chaps, I must say.'

'He's a bloody Pom, boys,' the soldier called out.

'But *I'm* the genuine article,' Tasman said from behind. 'And I reckon the Pom's right – it's good to see you.'

Kiwis, Aussies, Brits and Greeks now squeezed to the front to shake hands and pat the shoulders of Tasman and Smith, who were both overwhelmed by the reception. One man asked Tasman: 'What's the last cricket score you heard, mate?'

Tasman said: 'Last I heard, an Aussie/Kiwi team were playing Germany – and we were none for five hundred!' There was a roar of laughter.

The Greeks now broke out a supply of retsina acquired from Germans who'd stolen it. 'We take back what is ours,' one of the Resistance men said. 'The enemy who took it, they will drink no more.' The wine flowed all night and the men's cheerful exuberance warmed the hearts of Tasman and Smith.

In the morning Tasman gathered the somewhat hungover British Commonwealth soldiers together and explained that they'd be transported to Turkey and then, he hoped, be sent on later to Alexandria. In the meantime, they'd be safe in Turkey.

Through Smith, Tasman extended the same offer to the Greek soldiers. One of them spoke up.

'What did the bloke say, Smith?' Tasman asked.

'He thanked you but said they'll stay on here until there are more of them to carry on the fight.'

Tasman reached out and shook hands with the Resistance fighter, knowing they would never meet again after that day.

When darkness came the small group made their way down the mountain, Nicholas guiding them. They skirted Sfakia and moved eastward to the pick-up point. There they said goodbye to Nicholas, who seemed sorry to see them go. Tasman and Smith then led the men down to the sea cave where the raft was hidden. Standing on the rocks Tasman flashed his signal light offshore at intervals, as arranged with Ismail.

'He'll be there won't he, Millington?' Smith asked.

'If he can, Smith. If he can.'

'They will be there, Yuri. We must see them soon. Look beyond the darkness, they are there somewhere.' As the MTB made yet another pass along the coast Ismail was becoming very worried. It was now thirty minutes past the deadline and there was no sign of Tasman and Smith – no flash of light, nothing. Ismail knew that he might not be in quite the right position, and he refused to believe that anything had happened to the two men. He decided that the only thing to do was to send a signal himself; it would have to be visible along a stretch of the coast and far stronger than a flare.

He said to Yuri: 'Take two of the fuel drums and open them. I will come and help you in a moment.'

Yuri went astern and was getting the drums ready when he felt the deck move under his feet as the boat surged ahead. Ismail lashed the helm in position and hurried aft. Together they tipped each drum and let the petrol pour slowly over the stern and into the sea.

Ismail went back to the helm, eased off the throttles and turned the MTB broadside to the long track of fuel on the water, but at a safe distance.

The first flare from the Very pistol fizzled out as it hit the water. Ismail reloaded and fired again to a point further away. Suddenly the sea was on fire over a wide area. Surely Millington would see that, Ismail thought.

In fact Millington didn't see it, but one of the New Zealanders did. 'Look at that! I wonder what'... The soldier stopped as John Smith jumped to his feet.

'It's Ismail! We have to show him where we are. He's a bit too far to the east.'

'A fire, we need a fire quickly,' Tasman barked. The men swarmed up the cliff to the level ground above.

'Give us a match — have any of you blokes got a match?' The British soldier grabbed the box handed to him and tried to light the wispy grass. Seeing that it wasn't going to catch properly, one of the Australians ripped off his tattered shirt. That didn't work either. Finally someone produced a few scraps of paper, which flared the moment the flame touched them. The men added dry grass and the fire began burning well as others brought pieces of wood from around the plateau. Soon they had a large bonfire going.

'There is a fire, Ismail,' Yuri shouted. 'I can see it. There, that glow along the coast. Can you see it?' Ismail could see it and he knew what it was.

The first sounds of the MTB's engines brought a feeling of relief to Tasman, Smith and the men. Their raft could only carry five at a time, and as the MTB came to a stop offshore Tasman asked Smith to take the first four men out to it and then return to shuttle the rest to safety.

Within half an hour all the men were on board, including Tasman who was the last to pull himself up on deck.

'Millington, it is good you were not killed,' Ismail said as he pushed forward on the throttles.

'It is good you didn't get completely lost,' Tasman replied.

'Then it has been good for both of us, Millington.'

TWELVE

The brightness of the early morning light gave the soldiers on deck a sense that they were truly free from the hell of Crete. They were in good spirits and drinking coffee when one of the New Zealanders jumped up, shading his eyes with one hand. The aircraft came low and fast out of nowhere. So quick and quiet was its approach that it passed the MTB before Tasman could give an order to man the machine guns. Nor could he see its markings.

The plane climbed and turned for an attack run. Tasman held the bow steady until he could see the direction of the attack. The narrower the target the harder it was to hit. As the pilot aimed his plane at the starboard side of the MTB and began his run, Tasman hurled the wheel over and kept the bow facing the aircraft. The men on deck not manning the guns took cover where they could. The heavy fighter plane sent out a river of lightning from its cannons, shells ripping into the foredeck of the MTB. The plane peeled off at high speed, showing its RAF markings. To the pilot the boat's lack of identity meant that it must be treated as enemy.

Smith said to Tasman: 'That's a Bristol Beaufighter! They're well armed, and as fast as a Hawker Hurricane. Wonderful machine, don't you think?'

'I would if it wasn't trying to sink us,' Tasman snorted.

He then shouted at Ismail: 'Get the Australian flag – quickly!' They'd used the flag once before on an operation.

Ismail was climbing back through the hatchway when the Beaufighter opened up with another burst of fire. When it had passed he called to Smith: 'If you are killed by that plane you will know you were killed by a wonderful English machine, eh.'

'Where's that flag, Ismail?' Tasman grabbed it from him and, leaving the wheel to the Turk, sprinted down to the afterdeck. 'You blokes come here and hold this at the corners. Hold it up high in the direction the plane comes in. If he starts shooting, drop it and get down.'

Tasman knew there was a strong possibility that the pilot wouldn't see the flag in time. He looked at Yuri. 'Leave that gun! For God's sake don't fire back.' Yuri was happy to duck for cover under the engine hatch.

The Beaufighter was on its next run and swooping in very low over the water. Tasman took cover behind a row of iron plates the Russians had thoughtfully installed for such an occasion. But the gambit of using the Australian flag worked. The Beaufighter flew overhead without firing and circled back at much slower speed. The men on deck waved the flag wildly and others came out of cover as the pilot dipped his plane's wings in recognition before flying off toward the horizon.

'Well,' Smith said, 'there you are, Ismail. The English machine didn't kill me after all!'

Their spare fuel supplies were in Bozburun, but Tasman, wanting to get the men back, elected to bypass the safe haven and run straight up to Suvla Cove on a course well off the Turkish coast. It was a decision he would regret. While they were still well to the south of the Dodecanese island of Kos, Ismail and he sighted a schooner some distance ahead. It was sailing southeast.

'What do you reckon, Ismail?' Tasman asked. 'A fishing boat?'

Ismail wasn't at all sure. Along with caiques, schooners were often used for island trade. But he had heard from fishermen on the waterfront at Chanak that many of them were now heavily armed and being used by the Germans and Italians to supply troops stationed in the islands.

'Millington, I think it would be better to go around them,' he said. 'There may be great danger if we go near.'

Tasman considered the idea but knew that, if the schooner was in fact an enemy craft, its skipper would soon be making a detailed report on the strangely painted vessel he'd seen heading north into Turkish waters. They would have to take a closer look at the schooner even if it meant a conflict. Tasman ordered the soldiers to collect whatever weapons they could find below, and instructed Yuri and Smith to stand by the fixed machine guns, as he slowed down ready to intercept the schooner. Soon Tasman could see that it carried no flag or pennant of origin.

As the MTB moved closer, he had his answer. A heavy barrage of machine-gun fire erupted from the enemy vessel, hammering into the MTB's armour-plating. In reply, Yuri and Smith ran their machine guns hot as the soldiers' lighter weapons fired round after round. The concentrated fire from the MTB shredded the schooner's sails and tore into the rigging. Shattered pieces of timber fell to the deck. Smith and Yuri lowered their aim, firing at the hull which was now broadside on and drifting further away. Among the wreckage the enemy kept firing from at least four positions on board, but suddenly there was a massive explosion accompanied by a bright flash of light. A wave of heat rolled over the deck of the MTB. The explosion sent shrapnel flying in all directions, debris hitting the MTB and peppering its waterline.

When the air cleared, Tasman found that some of the soldiers had been wounded, but fortunately there was nothing serious. He sent someone to take care of them. Across the water, the remains of the schooner bobbed about on the surface. There were no bodies to be seen.

Tasman moved to the helm and got the MTB underway. After only a few kilometres, Smith's agitated voice came from the hatchway. 'Millington, come quickly.' Tasman hastily gave the wheel to the ever-present Ismail and went below. The reason for Smith's concern was evident – he was standing ankle deep in seawater. Machine-gun rounds had ripped a long line of holes in the hull just below the waterline, permitting a steady flow of water into the boat. Once again Tasman had the MTB gradually sinking under him. Yuri and two New Zealanders guessed what was wrong and scrambled down the narrow companion-way, carrying manual pumps and pulling hoses behind them. As the Kiwis got to work Yuri pushed past Smith and levered up a panel in the floor. The moment it came free a small tide of water boiled up from the bilges below.

Tasman called to Ismail to stop the boat. He could see that the situation was serious and becoming urgent. 'Yuri, pull up the rest of the panels,' he said. The boards removed, Tasman lay down on the floor bearers, water washing over him, and felt for the holes in the hull. 'They're as big as a two shilling piece,' he said at last. 'There's no way we can fix them at sea.' He stood up, told the men to get help with the pumping, and went back to the helm to look at his chart.

The small island of Sirna has four tiny satellite islands just southeast of it. In the fading afternoon light Tasman could see the faint outline of Sirna ahead, and decided to make for one of its minuscule neighbours and try to beach the MTB there. He told Ismail: 'We have to get the boat into shallow water.'

He pointed in the direction of the island. 'Get Yuri down to the engines, tell Smith and the others to stay on the pumps – everyone else up at the stern.' As Yuri ran past on his way to the engine room Tasman said: 'Keep a close eye on the motors, Yuri, we'll be running in reverse, a long way in reverse.'

Tasman looked again at the little group of islets in the distance. During all his years on boats there'd been near disasters, close shaves and occasional collisions, but he'd never had a boat actually sink under him. And the MTB was most certainly going to sink unless he could beach it. The engines rumbled as Tasman turned the MTB around, ploughing up the water below the transom, and then took the boat carefully northward in reverse. John Smith and the men below were suddenly in water up to their knees as the flood sloshed to the bow section and away from the stern. The engine room was relatively dry and with the propellers and rudder still underwater the MTB ran well enough under the circumstances.

Ismail came back smiling. 'Millington, all will be well, we will make it to the beach. I knew you would not allow me to drown in the sea – not with Smith!'

Tasman laughed. He'd noted the occasional bit of friction between the two, and had been glad that it hadn't seemed to affect their work.

Just as Yuri was getting worried about the heat and smell of the engines, the MTB came within twenty boat-lengths of the nearest islet's shore. A soldier standing at the side of the stern called out in a loud voice that the water was changing colour. That was good news but Tasman couldn't see a suitable place to beach the boat. Ismail piped up: 'There, Millington. A break in the rocks, can you see it?' Tasman saw it – a gently sloping area of sand not much wider than the MTB. He backed the boat toward the water's edge. Ismail turned to him with an inquiring look. 'Millington, will you not need to beach the *bow*?'

'I'd have to turn the boat about,' Tasman replied, 'and all that water down below would probably rush back and come up under the engines. No, we'll have to take her in stern first.' Tasman eased the MTB backwards, then cut the engines as the hull slid on to the sandy bottom and tilted at an uneasy angle.

The prospect of a moonless night put immediate repairs out of the question and, except for Yuri and Ismail who were on rotating watch, everybody got as much sleep as they could until daybreak.

After a few hurried mouthfuls for breakfast, Tasman went overboard to check the hull. Emerging from the chest-deep water he called to Smith: 'We can make plugs for the holes, and then we can pump the water out.'

'How many holes are there?'

Tasman walked up to him on the beach. 'I counted thirty-two – it's no wonder we almost went down.'

'I can make the plugs, mate,' said one of the British men. 'I'm a carpenter by trade.'

Tasman told him to remove suitable pieces of wood from the MTB's interior and to choose any helpers he needed. Tools left on board by the Russian workers were in a stern locker and Tasman asked Ismail to get them and also to find some canvas and cut it into pieces to wrap around the plugs.

Smith said: 'That schooner, Millington. Germans, Italians? Who do you think they were?'

'I don't know – it doesn't really matter, does it? Either way, they won't be going out sailing again.'

'Right, but I'm curious about the explosion. They must have been loaded up with a lot of ammunition.'

Some of the plugs were difficult to fit in place, as the bow of the MTB was out in deeper water. But Yuri came up with the idea of lowering a couple of sections of hose over the side so that the two men working there could use them as snorkels and stay underwater longer. Smith had taken his pump crew below and they were hard at work when Tasman stopped them. 'Don't pump the water out or the bow will rise and we'll never move this boat off the beach. Wait until we're off and floating.'

Finally the work was finished, but the real test was still to come. The Mediterranean seas have almost no tides and it would not be possible to simply wait for a high tide to float the MTB off. Tasman knew that he'd have to rely on a combination of luck and brute force. He went up to the helm and started the engines, leaving them idling in neutral. Then he ordered a dozen men to go to the sides of the stern, ready to what they could to both rock the MTB and heave it forward in stages. He was not optimistic.

Knowing that the propellers were in shallow water and very close to the sandy bottom, if not resting on it, Tasman shouted 'Here we go!' as he eased the throttles forward. The men strained at the back of the MTB, sand and seawater churning around their legs, and the boat slipped ahead a little. Tasman pushed the throttles down hard. The water boiled around the men, who gave the big craft a final mighty heave as it floated free, its bow well down.

Tasman took the MTB out a few metres and waited for the others to swim out and pull themselves aboard. The pump crew went back to the flooded lower deck. A little later Tasman examined the hull and declared it reasonably watertight.

The next stop would be Suvla Cove, and for every man on the boat it couldn't come soon enough.

THIRTEEN

At Suvla the Russian workers shook their heads when they saw what they had to do to repair the MTB – the gouged and broken timber, the bullet holes, the makeshift plugs keeping it afloat. But that night they listened wide-eyed to Yuri's animated story as he described the escape from Crete and the things he'd encountered coming back.

Tasman now needed to get back to Chanak, and the British Commonwealth men had to be told how to conduct themselves at Gallipoli while he was away. 'If I can have a word with you blokes,' Tasman began. 'Now you're here in Turkey you'll have to forget about the war for a while, until at some point we can get you away to Alexandria – or somewhere. For now, I think you'll all make pretty good gardeners here on the Peninsula. It'll keep you out of trouble.' He explained what would be involved, and then went on: 'Let me introduce you to Gino, one of the people who works here. He can help you. Now, a lot of you might think that Gino's an Italian, and that's because he is.'

One of the men said: 'I thought we were at war with the Italians, Major.'

'We are – but we're not at war with Gino,' Tasman replied.

In support of his own position Gino couldn't have agreed more. He stood up for a moment and faced the men. 'The colonel is right! I am Italian and for me the war is over.' He sat down again quickly.

'He's your prisoner then is he, Major?' the soldier asked. 'And why does he call you "colonel"?'

Tasman looked at Gino before he answered. 'It's a long story, my friend, a very long story.'

With Ismail and Smith, Tasman returned to Chanak leaving the Commonwealth soldiers in the hands of the Commission workers and under orders that they were to go nowhere near the straits side of the Peninsula. And for good reason: Gallipoli was getting unusually crowded.

A fortnight later John Smith came to the breakfast table from his room at Tasman's house. He said: 'You know that coded signal I sent to London? Well, they've answered it.'

Tasman waited but Smith didn't go on as he usually did. 'So, what did they say?'

'I said we'd been down to Crete and liberated some of the chaps there.' Smith stopped again.

'And?' Tasman was growing impatient.

'And they say you're now entirely on your own – and best of luck!'

Tasman looked at him. 'Did you give them all the information we gathered?'

Smith nodded. 'Yes, I did. I'm sure they're grateful for it.'

Tasman walked out of the house without saying a word. He wandered about the town until he saw Ismail sitting with another Turk, drinking tea and playing cards outside a café by the waterfront. Ismail beckoned to him. 'Millington, this man is Umit, a brother of my wife Zehra. He has brought news to me from the time we were away fishing in the south. Will you take tea with us?' Ismail waved at the waiter, then paused. 'The news Umit has brought concerns you, Millington.'

Hot tea in a tulip glass appeared in front of Tasman. 'What is it, then?' he asked.

Ismail answered in a hushed tone that Tasman should hear it from Umit himself.

Umit said: 'Mr Millington, there is talk here in Chanak – talk that you are a spy, an agent of the English King George.'

Tasman reacted calmly, although he hadn't expected to hear this. 'That's absurd, Umit! You and everyone here in Chanak know about me. You know I work for the Imperial War Graves Commission. No, I'm not a spy, I'm just an ordinary Australian bloke over here doing a job.' Tasman sipped his tea and for a moment wondered whether he really was still an Australian. But Umit hadn't finished.

'There is more, Mr Millington. They say the old army that lies under the ground over on the Peninsula ... they say they rise from the graves and walk and talk like living men. Some people here have seen them – so they say – but I do not for myself believe them.'

Tasman and Ismail laughed, trying to pass off this piece of intelligence. 'I'm afraid someone's pulling their leg,' Tasman said, still grinning.

But Umit persisted. 'They say the old army, some of them, still wear soldiers' clothing. And they play a game with coins they throw high in the air and they speak of heads and tails and something called a spinner.'

Tasman almost choked on his tea. 'Umit, these are the tales of old women. You are foolish to listen to them.'

Ismail added: 'Millington is a kind friend of the Turk and he is not a spy. He is an Australian from Tasmania and Hobart. He is not clever or smart enough to be a spy.'

'Thanks, Ismail,' Tasman said. 'I hope that's cleared up your concerns, Umit.'

'I am most sorry, Mr Millington, for having brought you the chatter of old women – not that I believed it. I did not believe it even when I heard that some of these old women had themselves played the game of coins with dead soldiers – dead men who said they were from your country.' Umit was laughing now too. 'Other old women say these dead men bought a large amount of raki from a farmer.' Leaning closer to Tasman's ear, Umit said softly: 'And it is good that these men are dead – too much raki makes the head spin and hurt very badly the next day!' He laughed again. So did Tasman and Ismail, continuing the charade.

But Tasman had very black thoughts about his charges living it up on the Peninsula, busily consuming aniseed-flavoured alcohol that was far more explosive than the enemy schooner he'd sent to the bottom of the sea. And not only that but they'd been playing two-up with some of the locals as well.

'Thanks, Umit. It's been good to meet you.' Tasman stood up and began to walk away.

After a moment Ismail trotted after him. 'Millington, where are we going in such a rush?'

Tasman looked over his shoulder. 'Go to my house, Ismail, and get the rations bag. We're going over to the Peninsula, right now.' Tasman strode down to the Commission moorings to get a launch ready.

It was well after nightfall when the pair reached the Suvla camp. They were both tired from their long trek over the Peninsula, and Tasman was very edgy as he walked into the flickering light of the men's cooking fire.

'G'day, Major,' one of the Australians said.

'G'day yourself,' Tasman responded. 'I want to talk to you blokes.'

Ismail sat down while Yuri poured hot tea from a billy.

'Have any of you seen anything strange over here – anything at all?' Tasman asked.

A New Zealander asked: 'When you say, have we seen anything strange, what do you mean?'

Tasman looked at the men. 'Oh, I don't know. Maybe a ghost or two floating around. Maybe the ghosts of some blokes playing two-up with the local farmers ...'

The group of men sat there, not saying a word. Tasman stood up and started to pace about, something that Ismail knew he did only rarely, when he was about to explode like his famed 'quake bomb'. 'Are you all out of your mind?' he roared. 'Keep to yourselves, I said.'

'Yeah, but Major ...'

'But nothing, Digger!' Tasman swung round. 'You blokes don't seem to grasp the situation we're in, all of us – you, me, Ismail, Smith, the War Graves Commission. We're in Turkey, it's a neutral country, and we're their guests.'

'Fair go, sir,' said a guilty Cockney voice. 'It's not as if we got drunk and swum over to Chanak, like.'

Tasman glared at the man. 'And now you mention being drunk, where's the grog you bought from the farmer?'

The silence around the fire equalled that of Gallipoli at its most sombre.

'We sorta drank it, guv'nor. We got a bit lonely, see, a bit depressed really, over here among all the poor dead lads from the Great War. But we did toast yer good health a few times 'fore it was all gone, Major. Sir, you was here in that war, wasn't you? It musta been awful!'

Despite his anger, Tasman had to suppress a laugh. 'Not as awful as it's going to be for all of us if you blokes can't follow orders and keep your heads down.'

'I'd like to say something too, Major, if I can,' a New Zealand Digger remarked. 'It's all been pretty hard, sir – the Germans drove us out of Greece, over to Crete, then the navy left us behind to surrender to the enemy and spend the rest of the war in a POW camp. Or else we headed for the hills and fought on. Then you come along and get us out and bring us here to safety. Now, I'm not saying we haven't been larrikins over the past few days, but there's not a man here who'd do anything disrespectful among all these cemeteries. Not here of all places, Major.' Tasman nodded and the soldier continued. 'I don't know about these other blokes – I was never much of a gardener anyway – but I came here to fight the enemy, and if there's any way possible I'd like to try and get somewhere I can rejoin a fighting unit.'

The others all agreed, and Tasman decided he'd forget the two ghostly incidents after getting an assurance that there'd be no repeat performances.

On the MTB later that night he thought about what the Kiwi soldier had said. The men had all come to fight the enemy, and the enemy wasn't far away. Tasman wondered if it was his duty to take them to the fight.

Big things were happening in Intelligence. Britain seemed to be well and truly winning that aspect of the war, at least at Bletchley Park where, by New Year's Day 1942, they had broken the German Enigma code used by the Luftwaffe High Command. Within days the decrypting specialists had also broken the German Air Corps code. But the single most important code used by the Germans was one that carried supply signals from Berlin to the Eastern Front. This code was soon in England's hands too.

The tide turned again, though, when only a month later the German Submarine Command changed its Enigma code and blinded Britain to vital signals in the Mediterranean and the Atlantic for the remainder of 1942. And in the Mediterranean the Allies needed all the help they could get.

In one instance, the Italian Navy sank four ships carrying fuel to Malta, while in the skies above there was a mere handful of fighters to repel attacks by 200 enemy aircraft. Similarly, of a group of 47 Spitfires sent to Malta, 30 were destroyed by German air attack. However, Malta enjoyed some relief on 9 May 1942, with Operation Bowery. The US aircraft carrier *Wasp* and the *Eagle*, a British carrier, had taken 62 fighter aircraft to a point about 1100 kilometres from the coast of Malta. The island's defenders waited ready to refuel the planes and get them back in the air as quickly as possible after the long flight from the carriers. On that day the fighters succeeded in intercepting all nine Italian and German air attacks made on Malta. By mid-July some 700 Axis aircraft had been removed from the skies by heavy ground fire and another 190 enemy planes had fallen as the result of dogfights with British fighters.

Elsewhere, Rommel had given up hope of taking Alexandria and Cairo in Egypt, and Allied gains in North Africa, though small, were taking a toll on the German war machine.

At this point in the war Hitler issued Directive 45 – causing British Intelligence more than a little concern. The Black Sea city of Rostov, which had been won back by the Russians, was again in German hands, and on 23 July Hitler issued orders to his forces to secure an oil supply by taking the eastern coast of the Black Sea from Novorossiysk to Batumi, through which much of the Caucasian oil trade passed. Batumi was right on the border of Turkey.

Bletchley's Enigma machine had decoded the orders sent to German commanders and a message reached John Smith in Chanak from his contacts in Istanbul.

'You'd better read this,' he informed Tasman. 'It looks as though the war's getting to be a bit of a worry northeast of here.'

Tasman read the message and then got out a map. Clearly a new phase of the war had begun. The Germans had been rampaging through Russia and they had long been threatening Turkey with invasion if it didn't comply with their demands. Now they were approaching Turkey in the northeast as well as facing it just across the border in Thrace, the eastern region of Greece.

'There'll be trouble, old man,' Smith said. 'If they get any closer they'll be knocking on your door.' He was studying the map on the table, a preoccupied look on his face. 'This railway line through Thrace, from Salonika to Alexandroupolis. Some of it's quite close to the coast and there are stretches that go through tunnels in the mountains. Very interesting, very interesting indeed.' Tasman could see Smith's mind at work.

Smith looked up. 'You don't fancy a bit of sabotage do you, Millington? Blowing up railway lines is a passion of mine.' He paused and then said:

'There's nothing *we* can do in the Black Sea, but Thrace – who knows?'

Tasman saw another possibility in the idea: that the Commonwealth soldiers bored with gardening at Gallipoli could now get back to war. It was agreed that Smith would work on a plan for a lightning raid.

When Tasman told Ismail of the proposed operation, the Turk's only comment was that he could see why Gino always said that for him the war was over.

The Russians completed their repairs to the MTB by the end of the month, and John Smith went to Suvla to look it over and to check a stock of explosives and other items kept near the Commission camp. On his return he guaranteed that he and Tasman could create quite a dent in the railway line. The aim in crippling the line, as Smith explained it, was to prevent the transit of enemy troops and their armour into and through Turkey. Yes, the Germans could rebuild the line, that wouldn't be too great a problem. But Smith said he hoped to make the job a big one. He was in fact contemplating bringing half a mountain down into a tunnel.

Tasman said he'd been thinking of something a little more spectacular. Smith gaped at him. Tasman grinned and said: 'I just meant, why not attack the railway in more than one place?'

Tasman had Smith's attention, so he pointed to the map. 'Here — west of Istanbul — see where the rail line runs north toward Uzunkopru?'

'That's in Turkish territory!'

'I can read a map, John. But what if, besides going to Thrace in the MTB, another team goes up near Uzunkopru by land. We could have two cracks at the line — wreck it in both places — and make it that much harder for the Jerries.'

Smith's eyes gleamed. 'Ever seen a train come off the rails at speed, Millington, with the wagons loaded with munitions and enemy soldiers? Wonderful sight it is!'

The map showed that the overland journey was about 70 kilometres each way from Suvla, all of it over rough and wild country north of the Peninsula. Smith asked: 'When do you intend calling for volunteers?' Tasman stared down at the map and didn't look up when he answered. Smith laughed. 'My good man, I rather thought you had already.'

Ten days later Yuri had rounded up the Commonwealth soldiers scattered among the graveyards and passing the war pulling weeds. They were assembled at Tasman's request at Baby 700 cemetery, the closest central point to where they'd all been working. Tasman and Smith joined them there.

That night, in the dull glow coming from the cooking fire, several of the men came up to Tasman and awkwardly told him how privileged they'd felt about being at Gallipoli and contributing to its upkeep. Tasman knew what they meant: it was a feeling that had never left him. In turn, he spoke of heroes, like those beneath their feet, and told the soldiers around him that those men would recognise them as equals.

Finally Tasman asked for the group's attention. After giving them a broad outline of the plan, he said: 'There's a good chance we might be able to put a small hole in the enemy. But I have to tell you that there's an even bigger chance that some of us won't make it back. Those who do will never be able to talk about it. For anyone who doesn't return, the best thing you can hope for is that British Intelligence will tell your families at some stage what happened to you, and perhaps where you're buried.'

The fire was rekindled a few times and large volumes of tea consumed as the men discussed the proposal. In the end one of the British soldiers called out to Tasman: 'The lads all say let's bring it on, Major. We'll go with you, sir.'

Tasman left Smith and walked toward the men. 'I don't have any official authority to give you orders on this operation – other than the field rank I have. But I'll tell you now that no man will be killed if I can help it. Now, let's get down to details.'

Daylight came before Tasman and Smith had the men fully clear as to their part in the plan.

While preparations were being made by the senior men, an intense daily battle raged at a small stretch of beach near Suvla. Australia were playing New Zealand in a long drawn out cricket match – the winner to play the English. The game helped to keep the men warm and occupied as the winter of 1942 descended on them.

John Smith went off to Istanbul again, this time to obtain information from his contacts regarding the German strength in Thrace. Almost from the moment he left the ferry he noted the marked increase in the number of European faces among the thronging crowds. At a café where he had a cup of tea he overheard some people speaking in German. To his surprise he heard them saying that Hitler was a fool and no longer able to lead the Fatherland to victory. And apparently, beyond the Black Sea, massive

German forces had been thrown at Stalingrad but the Russians were fighting back fiercely – so fiercely as to make a good Nazi wonder if the Russkies wouldn't soon be fighting their way through the streets of Berlin!

Smith spoke with his Intelligence contact that evening at the British mission, learning just how much out of contact they all were down at Chanak. His contact told him of the shift in supremacy in North Africa, with Germany and Italy suffering badly and Rommel, the 'Desert Fox', on the run with Allied soldiers at his heels. The contact confirmed what the Germans in the café had been saying about the Russians – that they were not going to give up Stalingrad, now or ever. And it seemed that this struggle was drawing in so much of Hitler's forces in the region that it placed his Directive 45 in jeopardy, making it unlikely that he would now strike at the northeast corner of Turkey.

Fortune had been kind to British Intelligence too. Bletchley Park was again able, after almost a year, to read the German U-boat codes, thanks to the heroism of three young men. The British Navy had been on the hunt for U–559 north of the Nile Delta, where on 30 October they caught and fired on it. The German commander ordered his boat to be abandoned and scuttled, but as it was being flooded Able Seaman Colin Grazier, Lieutenant Tony Fasson and a young galley hand, Tommy Brown, climbed into the sinking submarine and found its Enigma machine along with code books and other secret documents. Brown was at the top of the hatch as the other two men handed up the machine and pouch of papers. A moment later the sea swallowed the U-boat and Grazier and Fasson went with it to the bottom. Brown managed to get clear and was plucked from the water clutching the Enigma machine so tightly that it had to be wrenched from his hands. Lieutenant Fasson and Able Seaman Grazier were both awarded the George Cross posthumously. Tommy Brown was awarded the George Medal – and kicked out of the navy. Why? They found that the young galley hand was very young indeed, sixteen to be exact!

When Tasman heard Smith's account of the Stalingrad situation, he realised that there was little point now in risking political fallout from an attack on the railway line inside Turkish territory. But he thought the Germans might still decide to advance into Turkey from the west in order to put further pressure on the Turkish Government. To delay if not prevent any such advance, it was well worth attacking the line somewhere in Thrace. At the very least it would harry the Germans, who wouldn't be expecting it.

In mid-December, with the beach cricket over and Australia the victors, the operation was ready to begin. But the men knew that in war, even more than in peace, there was no guarantee of success.

Tasman and Ismail left Chanak for Suvla one biting cold morning to join John Smith and the soldiers, who for days had been making improvised explosive devices.

As they crossed the Peninsula, Ismail said: 'Millington, the old airfield near Drama. You know of it?'

'Yes, Ismail. What about it?' Tasman kept walking at his usual breakneck pace.

'Millington, will you please slow down for a minute while I take breath. I need to speak with you about the airfield.'

Tasman stopped a few paces further on and sat down on a rock beside the track. 'Well, I'm listening. What about the airfield?'

'If there are enemy planes there they will come after us. You have now decided, I think, that some men will stay on the MTB and others will go and blow up the railway and maybe collapse a mountain.'

'That's right, Ismail. Do you see a problem in that?'

'Yes, there will be a great problem. If we do not destroy the enemy planes – if there are any there – before the explosions, you can be sure they will attack the sabotage team and probably the MTB.'

It was such an obvious possibility that Tasman wondered why he and Smith had overlooked it. 'Why didn't you bring this up before, when I was revising the plans with Smith?' he asked.

Ismail got to his feet and looked at his friend. 'Millington, I did not wish to interfere with your ... faultless ideas.' They walked on and made the Suvla camp by twilight.

'He's right, you know,' said Smith when Tasman informed him. 'No telling what the Hun has got hidden away at the airfield.' He thought for a moment. 'I'll take my group as planned and head for the rail line. It's quite a distance, as we know. Now, what say you get to the airfield as soon as possible with some lads and do a job on anything you find there. And Ismail, Yuri and the rest can stay on board and look after the MTB until we return.'

Ismail stared at Smith and told him that he would not remain on the boat this time. 'I stayed on it when we were in Crete. No, I will go with Millington.'

Smith said: 'Well, I'm afraid it can't be me who stays. I'm the only one who can place the explosives for the rail job.'

Ismail wasn't going to be put off. 'Yuri can look after the boat – he knows it well. I will be going with Millington!'

In his planning, Tasman had plotted a course to take them out of the Gulf of Saros and to the west, where they would pass above the island of Thasos. His group going to the old airfield would now leave the MTB and make their way inland from a point west of Kavala, while the boat would head further around the coast with the second group, whose job was to destroy the railway line. Smith and Tasman agreed that the two attacks would be made at first light. Tasman's group comprised himself, Ismail and one of the Australians, a man named Joe. Smith's team was made up of the British soldiers and a New Zealander. The others would remain on the boat, with Yuri in temporary command.

The MTB slipped out of Suvla Cove in the wintry darkness. John Smith was down below with his men, checking the explosive devices and carefully packing them in haversacks, three of which would now be taken to the airfield by the other team. Ismail was also below, busily selecting weapons and ammunition.

There was no sign of activity on the coast or the water as they passed Thasos and cruised to the drop-off point just west of Kavala. Tasman handed over command of the MTB to Yuri, who'd been given his instructions, and together with Ismail and Joe he paddled ashore. They had a long, hard walk ahead of them. Ismail would have to keep up somehow, Tasman decided.

In the faint pre-dawn light at the airfield, Ismail said quietly: 'Millington, there are planes under those camouflage nets. See, beyond the hangar. Three larger planes and two smaller ones – they are probably fighters. I can see no guards.'

But Joe spotted a sentry. 'There! And there has to be more than one.' They watched the German for some time as he paced up and down. There would certainly be other guards but none were to be seen.

Ismail gave his equipment to Tasman. 'Millington, I will take him,' he whispered as the guard stopped by a stack of fuel drums and leant against them. Armed with his knife the Turk moved quickly to the rear of the stack and then crept around to the German from behind. The sentry died before he could cry out.

The three men raced to the nearest aircraft. No one challenged them. The plane was a Junkers JU–52. With Ismail helping him, Tasman put one of the explosive devices in place and set the timer, while Joe kept watch. The next net concealed a Junkers JU–88, the dreaded Stuka dive-bomber. Further along there were two more JU–88s and another Stuka. All received the same treatment. This raid wasn't exactly going to ground the Luftwaffe, Tasman thought to himself, but at least the five aircraft had done their last day's work for the Führer.

Dawn came as they left the airfield and began the trek back to the coast. They had walked perhaps half a kilometre when a series of huge explosions sent smoke and flames billowing into the air, followed immediately by the sharp rattle of exploding ammunition. The three men turned around to watch.

Ismail said with a grin: 'Millington, do you think they will be angry?'

Tasman looked at him. 'Who?'

'The Germans, Millington, the Germans!'

John Smith stood quietly on deck, looking back at the shore. Something had gone wrong – the charges possibly, or the timers. Somehow he had failed to collapse the tunnel or even damage the line. There was nothing to be done: Millington and his team would be waiting to be picked up. But Smith felt a keen sense of having failed the man.

Near Kavala, Tasman came back on board and resumed command of the MTB. The men stood ready at the machine guns as the boat cleared Thasos and headed into the open sea.

Smith joined Tasman when Ismail moved aside to go up on to the superstructure. 'I'm afraid I have to report that the line's still intact,' he said. 'It's entirely my fault – I must have done something wrong.'

Tasman had guessed as much but had waited until Smith came to him. He was about to respond when Ismail shouted something and pointed to a large dark shape flying low and slow toward them over the water. As he called out, Ismail dived for cover.

The plane was an Italian Seagull flying boat, a long-range convoy-escort and reconnaissance aircraft armed with three machine guns. These guns began to fire as soon as the MTB was within range. The gunners on the MTB reacted immediately and sent a heavy hail of rounds at the lumbering plane, while

Millington turned the helm hard and the deck listed sharply. But the Italians found their mark, sending pieces of ruptured deck timbers flying. Two British soldiers who'd been at the stern and shooting at the Seagull with their rifles went over the side into the cold sea. Tasman saw what happened and continued his fast turn. As he was manoeuvring the boat to try to reach the two men, Ismail called loudly over the roar of the MTB's engines: 'He comes again!'

Tasman watched the plane turn into its low attack run. The men in the water were now between it and the MTB. The Italians opened fire, spraying the water and hitting the two struggling soldiers, who vanished from sight.

Smith was at the Vickers gun and fired at the wooden tail section of the Seagull as the plane roared past. Every other gun and rifle on deck was sending up a storm of rounds. Then one of the Seagull's wing floats ripped away and crashed into the sea below. Part of the tail section shattered a moment later. The plane rose steeply, its engine lumbering under strain, and a hundred metres above the water it suddenly went nose up and stalled.

Even before the flying boat hit the water, Tasman had the MTB moving to the area where the British soldiers had been. Ismail, Smith and several others lined the bow deck at either side and scanned the water. But there was no sign of the men anywhere.

The MTB returned to Suvla, where the Russian workers helped fasten the lines. They could see that something had happened. Yuri quietly told them about the dead men as Tasman led the way to the camp. Everyone sat pensively, sipping hot tea. The air seemed to get colder and Ismail put more wood on the fire.

'I am sorry, Major.' Yuri's voice startled everyone. 'These men, my Russian comrades, they say they will be most proud if all of you will join us in drinking a salute to the men who died. It is rum from the barrel of our dead comrade, Joseph. We wish to recognise the bravery of the two English Cossacks ... with your permission.'

Tasman smiled at him. Tin cups were filled with the rum, emptied, and refilled. There were many toasts. 'English Cossacks, eh?' Tasman said. 'Yuri, I reckon those two blokes would have liked that!'

FOURTEEN

The worldwide anarchy wasn't at all evident in Chanak. Nothing much ever seemed to change there. Old buildings still lined the foreshore, many of them once consulates of great nations. Flagless poles still stood on shoreline and forecourt alike, reminders of what had once been important elsewhere. But old Chanak had chosen to ignore it all and just remain. The markets and bazaars, the smells and sounds, the fishing boats that came and went from the waterfront, the cafés with their endless glasses of tea, the old men playing cards, and the younger men coated in oil wrestling one another in Yagli Gures contests – all this was old Chanak and Tasman loved it.

At the main bazaar, he went to see Ildeniz about once a month to purchase his supply of tobacco and gummed papers. Although Tasman had long spoken the Turkish language, Ildeniz – like many other local people of whom Tasman had become a respected friend – preferred to converse with him in English. Ildeniz would listen carefully to everything the Australian said, looking for new words and expressions, and Tasman always tried to speak clearly so that the Turk could try out and repeat words without error.

One morning Ildeniz asked Tasman to join him for a glass of hot tea. They made passing comments about the cold weather, and then the Turk said: 'Mr Tasman, I have been able to get your usual tobacco from my last trip to Istanbul, but I regret this month it is more expensive. It is the war, you know. If it does not end soon it will bugger up my business.'

'What did you say?' asked Tasman.

'The tobacco – it is more expensive.'

'No, no,' Tasman said. 'What did you say after that?'

Ildeniz looked at him, puzzled. 'Oh yes, the war. Yes, it will bugger up my business. Why do you ask?'

'No reason really,' Tasman said as he finished his tea and stood up. He collected the tobacco and went down to the waterfront.

'Millington!' Ismail said, somewhat surprised to see him walk up to the table at the café. 'Do you know Turgut – a brother of my cousin's wife?'

Tasman shook hands with the smiling man as Ismail asked him to sit down and drink tea.

'I've already had some, thanks,' Tasman said. 'With Ildeniz in the bazaar.'

'And how is our good friend the tobacco trader?'

'He said the war is buggering up his business.'

'The war is a heavy burden to all of us. Do you not agree, Turgut?'

Turgut did agree. 'If the war does not end soon I think we will all be buggered.'

There was a short silence.

'Ismail,' Tasman asked, 'how long have we known each other?'

Ismail reflected for a moment. 'Well, it is a very long time.'

Tasman rolled a cigarette using his fresh tobacco. 'How many other people here in Chanak are using my colourful Australian words – which I have never spoken in front of them?'

Ismail's silly grin spread over his face. 'Millington, I'm buggered if I know!'

Not that Tasman hadn't thought it before, but this war was getting longer by the day.

It was a bad winter. The Peninsula was windswept at the best of times and at Suvla the soldiers would be feeling the harshness of the cold. As the Turkish and Russian workers were usually stood down from their labours for the War Graves Commission during the worst of each winter, the soldiers over there wouldn't be able to stay either. Tasman decided to take the risk of bringing them to Chanak. A group of Russian volunteers agreed to remain at Suvla to keep watch on the MTB.

As Christmas 1942 came and went and 1943 began, Tasman's house was almost bursting at the seams with the crowd of visitors. The men were well looked after by Mrs Millington, who never questioned for one moment that they were representatives of the Imperial War Graves Commission who'd come to conduct a survey of the tracks on the Peninsula. John Smith had all but kept to himself in the house for a couple of weeks after the operation in Greece, but now he became more like his old confident self.

Early in January a messenger came to Tasman's door. The man was a staff member of the Vali, the

Governor of Chanak, and he brought news that two bodies dressed in the uniform of the British Army had been found on the shore near Troy. The Governor thought they should be handed over to Tasman and the War Graves Commission. Ismail, Smith and two Australians went down in Ismail's truck to collect the bodies, which they believed had to be the British soldiers lost over the side of the MTB almost a month before.

When the recovery team reached Troy there was no doubt, although the bodies were in a sorry state. Extraordinarily, the dead men had drifted in the cold Aegean currents all the way from Thasos to the Turkish mainland, bypassing several islands as they were carried along.

Ismail had brought sailcloth to make shrouds. The bodies were carefully wrapped and solemnly carried to the back of Ismail's truck. When the group got back to Chanak late at night, Tasman told them he had decided that the British soldiers should be buried at the Haidar Pasha Cemetery on the outskirts of Istanbul. That cemetery was under Tasman's official control, whereas the old English cemetery in Chanak – which contained the graves of consulate officers and family members dating back to the 1860s – was not. Tasman knew that he was being particularly cautious but would not risk adding to the rumours around Chanak.

The bodies were discreetly conveyed by boat to Istanbul, where an honour guard of the dead men's former comrades stood at the graveside as Tasman conducted a moving burial service. As the small group left the cemetery, Tasman made Smith promise that when he eventually returned to England he would try to locate the men's families and tell them what had happened.

Far away in England, Naval Intelligence were putting together a truly remarkable deception against the Germans. The key to the plan was a dead body. It had to be one of a man who'd recently drowned or at least had a quantity of fluid in his lungs. A suitable corpse was located and Operation Mincemeat was put into effect. The dead man was given an identity and a rank – Major William Martin, Royal Marines – and dressed in a uniform. A briefcase handcuffed to his wrist contained secret documents showing that a strong military force building up to invade Sicily was just a ploy to blind the Germans to the Allies' real plan to land in Greece. On 30 April 1943 the dead 'major' was put over the side of a British submarine close to the Spanish coast where, Naval Intelligence hoped, the currents would take the body ashore.

The deception worked, although some German Intelligence officers vigorously questioned the authenticity of the find. Within a fortnight Berlin was sending a secret signal to its naval commanders in Greek waters, informing them that the Allies were going to land at Kalamata and Cape Araxos in the south of Greece, and adding that the code name the Allies had given the impending landings was 'Husky'. This was in fact the code name for the landings – but they were going to be in Sicily.

The German naval command in Greece acted quickly to shore up the hole in its defences, laying minefields and calling for reinforcements. The 1st Panzer Division was brought from France to Greece in preparation for an attack that wasn't coming. British cryptographers reading the Enigma signals knew that 'Major Martin' had fooled the Germans.

Although John Smith remained in wireless contact with London when relay arrangements permitted, he was given no warning of what was happening or that a squadron of German torpedo boats were making their way out of Sicilian waters and into the Aegean.

These E-boats, as they were known by Allied forces, were fast and diesel-driven as well as being heavily armed with surface weapons. They were formidable attack craft.

With the days and nights much warmer the Commonwealth soldiers had returned to Suvla, trying to look like Commission workers in the extra clothes they'd been given before Christmas. Tasman wasn't sad to see the back of them, as they hadn't been entirely confined to the house and questions could have been asked – and probably were, though the men had come to no harm.

Smith appeared at the Commission moorings in Chanak one day with a question for Tasman on his mind. 'Millington, have you ever thought of taking the MTB out to have a look at the enemy's supply lines to the islands down south? It's occurred to me that that schooner we ran into on the way back from Crete … the enemy would be using craft of that sort to supply their men on the islands, don't you think?'

Tasman had long assumed that the armed schooner they'd sunk wasn't the only vessel making a regular supply run. 'I think you're right, John,' he said seriously. 'But what can we do about it? We were lucky last time – that schooner was armed with better firepower than we have.'

Smith pulled a sheet of paper from his pocket and opened it out so that Tasman could see it. 'I've given this a bit of thought and I believe I've come up with a solution.' He pointed to the drawing of the MTB he'd made. 'You see here, and here, and again here.' Smith pointed out the marks he'd made at the bow, the stern and a point just aft of the helm. 'If the Russian chaps could build swivel cradles at these points the heavy machine guns could be mounted in pairs, each pair with an improvised central trigger mechanism. We'd be much better able to concentrate all our fire on the target.'

Tasman took the drawing and examined it for a while. 'I hate to admit it, John, but it's not a bad idea, not bad at all.'

'So, what do you say, old man?'

Tasman handed the piece of paper back and smiled. 'Well, don't stand about. Get over to Suvla and tell the Russians what you want them to do!' Smith looked pleased. As he turned to go, Tasman said: 'And before we do much traipsing about in the Aegean, we've got to collect that fuel stashed away at Bozburun.'

When Tasman and Ismail stopped for the night at Suvla after a regular inspection of cemeteries, they found that Smith's idea about the machine-gun mountings had been very good indeed. The MTB now bristled with eight swivel machine guns that could be operated by four crewmen. They were located at the bow and stern and both sides of the boat amidships.

'You've all done well,' Tasman informed the Russian workers. Turning to Smith, he added: 'All we need now is an enemy boat to practise on!'

Back in Chanak they had a troubling surprise when Ismail returned from the fish market one morning with news that a fisherman had been talking about seeing German gunboats.

'He means armed sailing vessels, doesn't he?' Tasman asked.

'The man was quite clear, Millington. The German boats had engines, not sails.'

In the absence of current intelligence from London, Tasman and Smith could only conclude that the Germans might now be almost at the door of the Dardanelles. And if so, then Turkey was under further threat of occupation.

The MTB left Suvla a little after midnight. Once again its complement included the soldiers, along with Yuri, Smith and Ismail. As the boat passed the mouth of the Dardanelles, on its way south to Bozburun to pick up the long-hidden fuel for whatever action lay ahead in the Dodecanese islands, Tasman felt that the MTB was now a true fighting vessel. The Dodecanese group, among which were Samos, Leros, Kalimnos, Kos, Rhodes and Karpathos, were currently occupied by Italian units.

Ismail spotted the schooner not long after they'd left Bozburun early in the morning two days later, the fuel securely stowed on board. The sailing vessel was heading up through the islands. Tasman turned the MTB to intercept the vessel as his men manned their machine guns. The crew of the schooner were soon in plain sight and clearly wearing Italian uniforms. On Tasman's order the Australian soldier at the bow machine guns fired a short burst at the schooner's rigging, but there was no return fire. The Australian immediately ceased when the four Italians started waving their arms madly. As Tasman turned the MTB about for a second pass, the schooner hove to and one of its crew held up a white cloth to indicate surrender. Tasman cautiously eased the MTB forward and Ismail heard an Italian yelling out: 'Hello, hello!'

With the MTB alongside and secured to the schooner, two New Zealanders jumped aboard, both armed with Sten guns, while the Australian kept his gun aimed directly at the Italians standing on the deck. A quick check below and in the forward hold revealed no surprises. The four men were the only ones on board. But Tasman faced a dilemma, as Ismail quickly realised. 'Millington,' he said, 'tell them they cannot surrender. We already have one Italian prisoner back in Chanak. It is not possible to have any more!'

The Italians seemed to be quite happy with the situation. Finally Tasman asked Ismail to go aboard the schooner and get the Italians to pull down the sails, and then bring the men on to the MTB. When they came across the side, Tasman was suddenly overcome with a feeling of déjà vu as the Italian officer sprang to attention and saluted, then grabbed him by the shoulders and kissed him on both cheeks. Tasman was more than slightly taken aback. His sense of déjà vu surged when the officer said in an approximation of English: 'It is good you take me and my men. For us the war is over.'

Ismail cried: 'No, Millington, the war is *not* over and they are the enemy. We must shoot them or let them go.'

John Smith spoke up: 'We can't let them go. The game will be up for us if they report what they've seen.'

'Then we must shoot them,' said Ismail.

Smith was right, of course. As Tasman looked at the badly shaken officer he knew that he would have to make a decision and make it soon. Tied up to the schooner they were like a sitting duck if any attack came from the air. He told Ismail and Smith to go aboard and find out what the Italian vessel was carrying. Then he could formulate a plan.

When the pair returned, Smith said: 'Just a lot of tinned food, bags of flour and about sixty drums of diesel, I'm afraid. Nothing that we need at the moment.'

Tasman turned to the Italian officer and asked about the drums of diesel oil. It transpired that the fuel wasn't going to be landed on any of the islands but was destined for a German torpedo boat that the schooner was scheduled to meet that night, south of Samos. Apparently it was a regular run.

Tasman took Ismail and Smith aside and put an idea to them.

'You're not suggesting we take on a German gunboat, are you?' Smith asked.

'No, not at all. What I'm suggesting is that the Germans meet the schooner as planned.'

Ismail looked lost. 'Millington, how is it that the Germans can meet the schooner when we have it?'

Tasman explained that, the way he saw it, the Germans would be expecting to meet the supply vessel as usual, and if it was right where it was expected and on time, the German crew might be inattentive enough to come alongside without thinking twice.

'That's all well and good,' Smith said, but who's going to be on board the schooner?'

'Not a soul,' answered Tasman. 'It'll be a ghost ship.'

Ismail was unconvinced. 'The ship will still need a crew of ghosts to sail it there,' he muttered.

'No,' Tasman said, 'there'll just be Smith and me.' He looked at Smith. 'I'll want you there to take care of a little surprise for Jerry.' He left them to think about that while he went back to the Italian officer to get details of the schooner's planned rendezvous with the German torpedo boat, and to requisition the man's jacket and cap.

Knowing what Tasman had in mind, Smith went below to pick over their stock of explosives. After a

1146 Pte Tasman Millington 26.11

CEH/BR.

Gresham House,

Sharia Soliman Pasha,

C A I R O.

28th November 1932.

R.D.Hadfield Esq.,
 Returned Sailors & Soldiers
   Imperial League of Australia,
     Sydney,
       Australia.

Dear Hadfield,

Your letter of 28th September reference T.Millington. He is a native of Hobart, Tasmania, and came away with the 15th Battalion - He served all through Gallipoli and then went to France, where he was twice wounded, but saw the fighting through to the end.

In 1919, when I was instructed to get together the Staff for the Imperial War Graves Commission, Gallipoli, I met him at Australia House, and he came out to the Dardanelles in charge of the Motor Boats and Sea Transport.

He is a first class hand in either Motor or Sailing Craft and has had many hair-raising adventures in the Sea of Marmora, the Dardanelles and among the Islands of Mudros, Tenedos, Imbros and Mitylene, particularly in the years 1922-1923, when the Turks again threatened the Dardanelles and Smyrna was burnt.

On completion of the construction work, Mr.Millington took over the Commission's work in the Constantinople Area, and in 1930 was promoted Area Superintendent, Turkey.

He now resides with his Wife, whom he met and married in England, at Chanak.

He has one Child, a boy, who was born on the Peninsula and baptised on Anzac Beach, the boy is now at School in England.

Mr.Millington has become a good Turkish linguist and gets on exceedingly well with the Turks.   Anyone visiting the Peninsula will get a real Aussie Welcome from him.

Yours Sincerely
C.E. Hughes

Bernard 'Anzac' Millington. Tasman's son was born in Istanbul, christened on Anzac Beach and by age 10 could speak fluent Turkish. He was schooled in England. Millingtons still live in Hobart, Tasmania. (*Reveille*, 1934)

Previous page: Colonel Hughes's letter (published in *Reveille*, July 1934) gives more than a faint hint that he knew exactly what Millington's 'other' job was in Gallipoli. Hughes wrote him a letter in which he described Millington's adventures as being those of a 'pirate' and said that this could lead to the Turkish authorities thinking he was some sort of spy, 'as absurd as that may sound!'

Crete, May 1941. British warships aflame in Suda Bay following heavy attacks by German aircraft.

German paratroops drop from the sky onto Crete. The island was the last place in Europe to be freed. The Germans didn't leave until 15 May 1945, a week after the war had ended on the Continent. (*Illustrated London News*)

British prisoners-of-war on the move in Crete. Four years of captivity
followed, first on Crete and then in Germany.

German Junkers Ju 87 Stukas on their way to a ground attack during the Mediterranean campaigns. Athough these dive-bombers were no match for Supermarine Spitfires and Hawker Hurricanes, they still posed a great threat to Tasman Millington's operations off Crete and the Greek mainland. (RAF Archives, Great Britain)

An enemy schooner under heavy attack. Such vessels were captured and used by Italian and German forces to run supplies between the small islands under their control. When Tasman Millington and his men came upon these vessels they found them well armed, and one even tried to take on his much faster gunboat. (RAF Archives, Great Britain)

A Motor Torpedo Boat (MTB) similar to the one used by Tasman Millington for his operations in World War II. Millington's boat had been stripped of all deck guns and other heavy weapons to give it a 'fishing boat look'. However, its lines fooled few when it was observed from the air – the enemy knew exactly what type of boat it was.

De Havilland Mosquito. This heavily armed and fast aircraft almost brought an end to Millington's operations in the Aegean when its pilot attacked the MTB.

Suvla Cove, Gallipoli. Turkey provided a central staging point not only for Tasman Millington's operations but many other secret missions conducted by Allied forces, and this isolated cove on the Gallipoli Peninsula proved to be the perfect hiding place for Millington's boat during the war in the Aegean. The water tank in the foreground (a relic from World War I) is almost certain to be the same as that in which Millington's men kept weapons and ammunition.

To a temporary victor goes temporary spoils. A German tank and its crew patrol the streets of Athens, near the Acropolis. The Greeks, both soldier and citizen alike, suffered heavily under German occupation.

Short Sunderland flying boat. It was in such an aircraft that a very dangerous and daring run was made to deliver Major John Drakopoulos to Millington's MTB lying off the coast of Turkey. (National Archives of Australia)

The German Enigma machine, used to send the most secret of communications and orders. British listening stations intercepted the cypher signals and sent them to Bletchley Park, not far from London, where code breakers read the messages and relayed them to war leaders such as Churchill and front-line commanders.

The German top-secret Geheimschreiber
teleprinter that from late 1942 was used to send
high-level, top-secret messages from Berlin to
German commanders, mostly in Russia. The
secret German codes were broken by the
British, and afforded vital intelligence until the
end of the war.

talian Seagull flying boat of the same type which attacked Tasman
Millington's MTB. The Seagull carried three machine guns, two mounted
o the hull of the aircraft and the third being reached by a ladder and fitted
o the wing at the rear of the engine. (Time Archives)

A Messerschmitt 109 after a hard landing. Germany built a total of 30,480 Bf109s for the Luftwaffe and they saw action on every front during World War II. It was a Messerschmitt that attacked Millington's MTB off the coast of Greece, with fatal results. (National Archives of Australia)

Tasman Millington (centre) seen here with his driver (background) and a visitor (right), at Quinn's Post Cemetery on 22 May 1951. By the time Tasman retired in 1960, he had served 45 years in the service of his nation and caring for the war graves. (Commonwealth War Graves London)

MR. TASMAN MILLINGTON

Mr. Tasman Millington, O.B.E., has died at the age of 67. Until his retirement he had been in charge of the Commonwealth war cemeteries on the Gallipoli peninsula since he joined the service of the Commonwealth War Graves Commission in 1919.

Born in Tasmania on June 16, 1896, Tasman Millington's first sight of Turkey was his landing with the Anzacs on the Gallipoli Peninsula in 1915. He returned in 1919 to help build the cemeteries and memorials which the Commonwealth War Graves Commission constructed to commemorate his fallen comrades. He stayed to look after them until 1960.

At Canakkale, on the Asiatic shore of the Dardanelles where Tasman and his wife were latterly the sole foreign residents, his only contacts with the outside world were with the relatives and comrades of the dead on pilgrimage to the peninsula and the occasional visits of the Mediterranean Fleet. But his work was his life and he was wholly content; his wife, a keen botanist, found pleasure in doing water colours of the flowers and plants of the peninsula. Between him and the Turkish officials and people with whom he lived and worked there was mutual trust and affection.

Paradoxically, in view of his lonely life, he will be remembered by all who knew him as the friendliest of men, kindly, warm-hearted and entirely unassuming.

He was made O.B.E. in 1934 and, for his help to the French in tending their War Cemetery on the peninsula, an Officer of the Legion of Honour in 1950.

His wife, by whom he had one son who survives him, died in 1956.

'Mission over'. Tasman Millington's obituary. Courtesy of St James's Palace Records, London.

careful search he found there were no timers left, and he thought bitterly of the devices probably still sitting by the railway line in northern Greece. He would have to use fuses instead, even though it would mean leaving the schooner at the very last moment. 'Or even later,' he mumbled to himself.

Tasman told Ismail to get the small raft on board the schooner and then joined Smith to discuss his requirements. They called to one of the Australian soldiers to come down and help them, and together the three men carried a number of packages across to the schooner. While Smith got on with the task of placing the explosives and arranging the system of fuses, the Australian helped Tasman with the sails and then leapt aboard the MTB as Tasman shouted to Ismail to cast off and follow him.

The schooner headed north, Tasman following a course that would take them to the rendezvous point. They saw several other boats in the distance, but no one challenged them. After a while Smith came on deck to help with the sail settings. Tasman found the large craft strange to handle at first, but his early sailing experience in Australia came back to him and he soon adjusted to the behaviour of the helm. Smith went below again to look for something to eat; in a few minutes the pair were having an impromptu meal of cheese and dry bread washed down with some red wine of unknown Italian origin.

As they stood there Smith explained what he'd done with the explosives. He pointed to a line of fuse leading up from the lower deck. 'Terribly unreliable, these lengths of fuse,' he said. 'I've tested this stuff – sometimes it burns fast and sometimes it burns slow. Sometimes it smoulders a bit and then goes out. But the marks I've made along the line are at one-minute intervals – more or less.'

'More or less' wasn't what Tasman wanted to hear, but there was no way out.

'By the way, Millington,' Smith went on, 'when the time comes I'd better light the fuse. You'll be too busy to deal with it if it decides to fizzle out.'

They reached the rendezvous point an hour before the scheduled meeting at sea. It was now completely dark. Tasman asked Smith to drop the foresail, slowing the schooner down, and to turn on the bow, stern and rigging lights. Together they put the raft over the starboard side and secured it with a line. Tasman signalled the MTB to come alongside, saying to Smith: 'I appreciate your concern about the fuse, John, but I'll be doing this job on my own.' And he wouldn't hear otherwise, even when Smith gave him more good reasons for the two of them to remain aboard the schooner. 'No, there are some things I want you to do, John, as soon as you transfer back to the MTB.' He quickly explained what he had in mind as he put on the Italian officer's jacket and cap.

Ismail brought the MTB carefully alongside the moving schooner, remaining there just long enough for Smith to scramble aboard, then headed off at full speed in the direction of the Turkish coast.

Thirty minutes later the beam from a powerful searchlight appeared in the distance and was followed by the dull throb of diesel engines. Tasman moved to drop the schooner's other sails, then stepped to the side in the light of one of the rigging lamps. Almost immediately the searchlight picked him out as he waved and beckoned to the slowly approaching E-boat. The time had come.

Tasman casually walked down the companionway steps, where the fuse line lay. He had only a few minutes. Checking the marks Smith had made on the line, he counted them off and snipped the cord with a pair of cutters at the four-minute mark. Tossing the discarded length into a corner he lit the fuse, muttering a small prayer that Smith had done the job properly.

With the searchlight now angled at the gradually narrowing stretch of water off the schooner's port bow, Tasman moved to the other side and eased himself down into the raft, pushing it away from the hull with his foot as he got settled.

The raft was no racing scull. Tasman hadn't gone a great way when he saw the E-boat loom up at the far side of the schooner. He pulled desperately at the oars. The fuse was getting shorter by the second – at least he hoped so. Soon a few German crewmen were moving about on the schooner's deck, wondering what had become of the man who had waved to them only a few minutes before. Apparently they hadn't seen him go to the companionway, but in a moment, he knew, they would go below and discover the present he'd left for them.

Tasman wasn't sure which came first, the blinding flash of light or the deafening explosion. These were followed by a series of huge blasts that lifted the schooner clear of the water; then it fell back on the sea and broke in two. Tangled and burning rigging and sails crashed over the deck of the German boat, the men there screaming as their clothes caught fire and their skin melted like butter in the sun. Other men were in the water, but it too burned and broiled. Suddenly there was a further massive blast, far bigger than those before it, as the E-boat's ammunition and torpedoes exploded, sending fragments of hull and superstructure over a wide area.

The shock wave through the water threatened to capsize the raft and Tasman was lucky not to be hit by flying debris. Darkness finally fell again as the last of the fuel oil burnt itself out on the flat sea.

The glow on the horizon was sharply clear to Ismail and the men on board the distant MTB. Tasman had ordered that they not return to retrieve him until daylight, but Smith was quick to agree with Ismail that they should head back without delay. Pieces of floating wreckage told them they had reached the area in which the two vessels had been, but there was no sign of Tasman. Ismail sent the MTB in ever widening circles, occasionally bumping into floating timber and other remnants. Hours passed but Ismail would not give up. Then, as light began to grow in the east, they spotted the raft with Tasman standing up and waving the Italian's tunic to attract their attention.

'You took your time,' he said after they'd hauled him up on deck. 'You passed close by me three or four times during the night and I shouted out, but you didn't hear me.'

Ismail shook his head. 'I told Smith the music he was playing on his gramophone was too loud. All we could hear was someone called Vera Lynn singing about the white cliffs of Dover!'

As Ismail swung the boat on to a heading that would take them back to Bozburun, he gave his skipper a cheeky grin. Tasman snorted. 'I hope you're joking,' he said.

Safe in the bay at Bozburun, and before any further expeditions could be considered, Tasman had to decide what to do with the Italians. They had willingly surrendered without a fight and the officer had been very forthcoming with the information needed to intercept the German E-boat. That counted in their favour.

Finally Tasman said to Smith: 'Try to explain to the officer that he has two choices. I'm prepared to set them adrift in a raft within range of one of the occupied islands, where they can rejoin an Italian unit, or I can give them water and provisions for a week and put them ashore here in Turkey. If they're discovered, which they're bound to be, the Turkish authorities will most assuredly incarcerate them for the duration. Anyway, ask him what they want to do.'

Smith began to object, but then thought better of it. After a good deal of talking and gesturing among the Italians, he came back to Tasman. 'The officer says they are no longer at war and they would like to go ashore here. He says that being a live deserter is much nicer than being a dead hero.'

Ismail was also displeased with Tasman's decision, but there was little he could do about it.

Early that evening the Italians were dropped off at a stony beach along the coast. 'What do you think will happen to them?' Smith asked.

Tasman said: 'I think they'll wander about a bit until the local police hear about them. There won't be many questions and they'll wind up in some sort of prison until the war ends.' He looked at Ismail. 'Better than being shot, don't you think?'

FIFTEEN

In July 1943 Italy's Benito Mussolini was overthrown and imprisoned. Although later rescued, his real authority had gone; power was restored to King Victor Emmanuel. Everywhere, in fact, the fabric of the Axis armies was falling apart. With the surrender of Italian and German forces across the Mediterranean in Tunisia, some 250000 men were taken prisoner; the once unstoppable Afrika Korps of Rommel, which for three years had owned the desert, was finished. In Russia the tide flowed in the defenders' favour. And high in the ranks of Hitler's close commanders there was real doubt that they had any chance at all of winning the war.

In early September Italy surrendered, putting its people on the receiving end of Nazi savagery. Tens of thousands died. The Luftwaffe sent air strikes against the Italian Navy, which was attempting to surrender in Allied-held ports. In Italy itself the Nazis withdrew more than 50 000 prisoners of war being held there, as well as taking 300 000 Italians to Germany as slave labour. At the Greek island of Rhodes 7000 German troops put an end to the Italian wartime occupation.

On 3 October a floodgate of sorts opened in front of Tasman and his men, who were now back at Chanak and the Peninsula. The Germans ordered that all Jews in Greece must register, and the Resistance, knowing what the outcome would be, made an all-out effort to prevent any further deportations to the Nazi gas chambers. The people of Greece responded, risking everything to hide Jews, and before long more than 3500 Athenian Jews were being hidden under the roofs of non-Jewish Greek citizens. The Greek Underground looked desperately for means to get Jews and others who were in immediate danger off the mainland and to safety.

During one of John Smith's transmissions with London when the relay allowed, he was sent a coded signal and to his surprise it was directed to him and not to Millington. The signal set up an Athens contact for him – a Resistance man he'd been working with when he was first sent out to Greece. The rest of the message was straightforward and Smith rushed into Tasman's kitchen waving a decoded version for him to read.

After all but ignoring Tasman and Smith's precarious situation for so long, London had now sanctioned a clandestine escape route through Turkey and thought they could help with it. And in fact they could. When Italy surrendered and British troops took over some of the Dodecanese islands, Tasman had decided to make fewer sweeps of the Aegean off the Turkish coast, as the supply vessel traffic had fallen off significantly.

The proposed new operation was anything but simple. The Greek partisans would acquire boats at their end under the nose of the Germans. Having done so they would smuggle Jews on board and put out into the Aegean in the direction of the Turkish coast. When safely landed the Jews would make their way through Turkey and on to Palestine, a destination now firmly in the hands of British Commonwealth forces. The risks in the scheme were great, but the risks of not trying the operation were even greater and certain to be fatal to the Jewish people and those who hid them.

'A lot of the boats aren't going to be too seaworthy, John,' Tasman remarked when they discussed the plan. 'They'll never get right across the

Aegean. I'd see our part in it as meeting them halfway – the Resistance gets the people out and brings them to a point where we can put them on the MTB. We've got a good chance of getting a lot of those people away, you know. Get on to your man in Athens and tell him we're ready when he is.'

Smith informed his contact of Tasman's 'halfway to home' plan and full-time monitoring of the radio was set up.

Tasman had a surprise of his own one morning when Ismail knocked on the door, accompanied by Gino, their ostensible POW.

'Millington, Gino wishes to make a request,' Ismail said, 'and he will not speak of it to me, only to you.'

'What is it, Gino?' Tasman asked.

'Colonel, I have been told by the Australians and also by the New Zealand men that Italia has given up the war and the Duce Mussolini is no more. I was never one of the Fascisti, Colonel, and now the German pig is more my enemy than he was before. Mr John has told me that the German has turned on the Italian with great evil.' He paused, looking at Ismail for a moment. Then he went on: 'Colonel, I have known for a long time that you and your men go out on the sea in the gunboat to hurry up the end of the war.'

'So, Gino, what exactly do you want?'

'I want to say to you, sir, that I am very – how do you say – accurate when I fire a gun. I would like to go on the boat with you and kill our enemy, the German.'

'Millington,' Ismail interjected, 'you will not think of letting an Italian join us on the MTB?'

'I can't see any reason why he shouldn't come with us,' Tasman said. He smiled as Ismail walked off muttering: 'Silly bugger, why don't we also get a German to join us?'

The occupation of Rhodes and Karpathos by German garrisons had forced the deferral of the British plan to move to mainland Greece in stages. But Kos, Leros and Samos were the targets of more than 250 Allied aircraft based in North Africa and Cyprus, as were German-held airfields in Crete and mainland Greece. The Germans took and held islands, the Allied forces took them back and then lost them again. By mid-October the skies above the Aegean were thick with Allied aircraft, including B–25 Mitchells from the American 310th Bombardment

Group escorted by British Beaufighters from 603 Squadron out of Libya. They attacked any vessel that floated in that part of the world.

Going into the Aegean in an unidentified motor torpedo boat was little short of suicide, but Tasman and his crew, including Gino, were now on their way out of Suvla Cove with only a single Australian flag fluttering from the short mast. They were heading to a designated interception with a caique carrying a couple of Greek partisans and fourteen Athenian Jews who had been living in hiding since the German decree of early October.

Staying in Turkish waters until the last moment, the men aboard the MTB watched a couple of furious air battles that reduced Allied planes to wreckage on the water. This first run to meet a caique and its passengers resulted in Tasman's men fishing a Beaufighter crew from the sea and taking them with them to the interception.

They came on the caique right on dusk and transferred the Jewish people to the MTB. After Smith had spoken with the two Greek partisans the old and weary vessel puttered back in the direction of the Greek mainland, its work far from done.

There was a scheme in place for the onward journey of the Jewish exiles, but the aircrew were a different matter – they wouldn't be able to travel the same route. After consultation with the pilot it was agreed that they'd be put ashore at Izmir, where they'd simply report to the authorities who would no doubt intern them until they could be repatriated. The sight of British airmen decked out in shorts must have been quite something as they walked through Izmir looking for a police station.

Many Greek Jews, of course, chose to stay in their homeland. These people too were hidden by caring Greeks, one of whom was the great-granddaughter of Queen Victoria – Princess Andrew of Greece, the mother of Prince Philip RN. She took Jewish people into her house in a bid to hide them from the Germans. But the flow of those wanting to escape continued. The MTB's trips became more and more frequent toward the end of 1943 and by January Tasman was making a run every ten days.

Other escape routes were being operated in the Aegean at the same time. Tony Simonds used small craft to liberate some 700 people from the clutches of the Germans during December and early January. They included several hundred Allied soldiers taken off Leros, Samos and Kos and then smuggled into Turkey.

Searching for a vessel operated by the Greek Resistance one night, Tasman saw a caique in the distance and assumed it to be the one he was looking for. When he got closer the heavily armed craft opened fire on the MTB and Tasman's men were caught off guard. They weren't at their heavy machine guns. The MTB took damage above its waterline and it was only by good fortune that no one was killed or even wounded. The men were quickly at the gun mounts and returned a massive volley of rounds at the other boat, shredding it into wood chips as the MTB made repeated runs at it. The German crewmen were still at their guns when the caique caught fire and began listing severely. After Tasman made another high speed run at it, with the MTB's machine guns aiming below its waterline, the vessel rolled over and sank almost immediately. There were no survivors. The crew had all gone down with the caique.

The 'little war' in the Aegean was increasingly being fought by small clandestine groups and even individuals. Soldiers on the run and Resistance fighters, along with civilian men and women, were doing all they could to harry the Germans. But British Intelligence were active behind the scenes. They had a renewed interest in Crete by April 1944 and a particular object of their interest was the German general in command of Crete, Heinrich Kreipe.

The Special Operations Executive sent two agents – Major Patric Leigh-Fermor, who was dropped into Crete by parachute, and Captain Stanley Moss, who was quietly brought ashore by the Greek Underground – to make contact with Resistance fighters and get information and assistance. On 26 April General Kreipe, who'd been at his headquarters in Arhanes, was driving back to his house near Heraklion when the unexpected happened. The British officers captured him and then set off on foot across the island. Seventeen days later they reached Rodakino on the south coast, from which they took Kreipe by a circuitous route to London. The British let it be known to the general's staff in Crete that, should there be reprisals, they'd not be able to guarantee that Kreipe wouldn't meet with an unfortunate accident. The Germans were well versed in people having accidents and initially they did nothing. But a few months later they pillaged both Kedrous and Anoya, murdering over 500 Cretan civilians in a frenzy of revenge.

The story was no different for the Germans' former ally, the now hated Italians. They were slaughtered too. The Nazis were unable to come to grips with the surrender of Italy, and anyone not on the German side could only be their mortal enemy. But on the Italian war-front, Monte Cassino and Anzio, a little to the south of Rome, were finally breached by the Allies and the push toward and beyond the capital began. This complex operation caused considerable losses.

On 6 June 1944 the biggest seaborne invasion in history began at Normandy in France. Eighteen thousand troops parachuted in at first light and the beach landings began at 6.30 that morning. Hundreds of thousands of soldiers had come to defeat the Germans, and the Germans had been fooled as to the Allies' intentions. The D-Day landings were a triumph of secrecy and planning.

But down in Crete, D-Day had and will always have a very different meaning. As the sun climbed higher that morning, German troops were loading an old ship with people they'd rounded up. More than 400 Greeks and Cretans, 250 or more Jews, and well over 350 Italians taken as 'prisoners of war' after Italy's surrender were packed in like sardines. The ship was towed far out into the Mediterranean, where the Germans sank it with over a thousand people on board, leaving them to drown.

Only a week later another 2000 Jews on the island of Corfu were rounded up, sent to the Greek

mainland and put on a train for Auschwitz, where all
but a hundred or so were taken straight to the gas
chambers – that is, those who weren't already dead
after the two-week rail journey from Greece.

These atrocities led to renewed efforts by Greek
Resistance people to get their Jewish charges across to
Turkey. Early in August John Smith received an
urgent request from his contact in Athens. He told
Tasman afterwards: 'They say there's sixty-four people
to come over. The poor things can't remain there any
longer and the Resistance can't get them out at the
moment because they've got a shortage of boats.'

Tasman said: 'Well, in that case I suppose we'd
better get the team together and go and get them
ourselves.' After looking at his charts he turned back
to Smith. 'Signal your bloke in Athens and ask him to
get those people up to Marathon and then out to the
coast. We'll pick them up there. At noon, four days
from now.'

This wasn't just a risky mission into the Aegean, it
was like waving a red cape at the German bull. A plan
began to form itself in Tasman's mind and he went in

search of Ismail, hoping that the Turk's extended family would rise to the occasion once more.

Tasman wanted several German uniforms made, to be worn by himself and those of his men who would remain on deck when they reached Greece, plus a Nazi flag for the MTB.

Ismail had learned more and more over the years that there was no changing Tasman's mind when he'd made it up. 'The flag and uniforms can be done,' he said, 'but Millington, the caps, the badges – how will I get them?'

'Don't worry about it,' Tasman grinned. 'I don't plan to get that close to the enemy.'

Three days later in Suvla, Tasman laid out the operation for the Commonwealth soldiers. They had concerns but they all volunteered to go. 'There's one other matter,' he added. 'When we get these people to Turkey I want you to go with them and see them safely into Palestine. You'll be able to join up with our blokes when you get there – you've all been on holiday too long!'

With final preparations completed by Ismail and Yuri, the MTB – now manned by a crew that Smith described with a smirk as 'the Führer's fearless flatfooted fighters of the Fatherland afloat' – pulled out of Suvla and headed straight to sea. The three soldiers wearing

German uniforms amused themselves by combing down their fringes and giving one another Nazi salutes. Tasman kept the Australian flag flying until they were within range of the Greek coast, then changed it for the despised Swastika emblem as they entered the wide channel between the islands of Evvoia and Andros, east of Athens. The MTB rounded the headland there and moved into the Gulf of Petalion. Marathon lay at the top of the Gulf, a little inland.

Tasman ordered his crew not to man the machine guns. These waters were held by the Germans and standing at the guns might give the game away if other boats came close. They did encounter other vessels but none of a military type. After passing freely up the Gulf to the narrows near Marathon, Tasman stopped the MTB in a tiny cove.

They could see the refugees on the shore, a few at first, and then more came out from behind rocks where they'd been sheltering. A New Zealand soldier rowed the raft in and began to transfer the 64 people, five at a time, until they were all aboard the MTB – as many of them down below as could be fitted in.

It had all gone very smoothly, Tasman thought. There was a last wave from the armed Resistance men on the shore and he soon had the engines up to speed as the MTB left the area.

Shortly after they passed the headland they saw a German coastal patrol boat heading through the channel toward them.

'Millington,' Ismail said, 'what will we do? This is the enemy you didn't plan to get close to!'

Tasman was silent. The number of people on deck was a definite problem. In fact, everything about the MTB was likely to draw the patrol boat's attention. He called to Smith. 'Go up to the bow, John, and stand by the double gun – and smile. Give the Nazis a big wave and I'll steer as close as I can.'

'And after I wave to them, old man?'

'Give the gun barrels a bit of a run-through. The salt water does a lot of damage to them!'

'Quite so. Yes indeed, that's quite so, Millington.'

The small patrol boat had only four crewmen that Tasman could see. Smith was at the bow of the MTB. And standing at the helm Tasman heard the midships guns being readied by Gino and one of the soldiers. As the patrol boat came near, Smith waved and the Germans waved back. In a moment or two they were off the MTB's port bow. There was a loud chatter from Smith's guns as he sprayed the other boat with heavy fire, followed by the racket of the portside midships armament. Pieces flew off the German craft from stem to stern and the crewmen, caught by surprise, collapsed over the railings or fell bloodied and dead on the deck.

Tasman took the unscathed MTB swiftly through the channel and out into the Aegean. When they cleared the island of Skiros he had Ismail take the helm while he went to the short mast and took down the German flag. As he began to hoist the Australian flag in place of the Swastika he was stopped by a young Greek Jew. The boy took the line from Tasman's hands and with a proud smile ran the flag up to the mast top himself.

They passed south of Khios and reached the coast of Turkey near Kusadasi, where the jump-off point for the escape route was situated. Within a matter of days the refugees would be in Palestine and safe. There were heartfelt thanks from them all as they went ashore knowing there'd be no SS troops to drag them away. And there were grateful thanks too from the British Commonwealth soldiers who'd come so far with Tasman. They all knew the need to keep his operations secret and they gave their word on it.

'It's still summer and there's still five of us, Millington,' Smith said as they moved through the calm water back to Suvla. 'An Australian, an Englishman, a Turk, a Russian and an Italian. Fancy a spot of French cricket when we arrive?'

SIXTEEN

Athens was liberated by British soldiers on 13 October 1944. But there were difficulties in Greece: the Greek communist forces were a power in themselves, having begun a civil war against the government, and as Christmas came around they were in almost full control of Athens. Winston Churchill himself flew to Greece and persuaded the communists to throw in their lot with Archbishop Damaskinos. From Britain's perspective this prevented a postwar communist regime emerging in the Aegean.

In Chanak Tasman and his wife had another house guest over Christmas. Besides John Smith, Gino the Italian sat drinking raki with them and wondering how much longer the war would last. In the ensuing weeks Tasman concentrated on his real job at Gallipoli. The winter of 1944–45 was proving a mild one and with the Greek Jews safe from the Germans he and his workmen were able to catch up with jobs in the cemeteries that had long been left undone. The MTB, meanwhile, sat idle under its camouflage nets at Suvla.

In Berlin Hitler was still issuing futile orders to his few surviving senior commanders when the Russian Army seized the Reichstag, only a kilometre or two from his bunker deep below ground at the Chancellery. But at half past three on 30 April 1945, ten days after his fifty-sixth birthday, Hitler put a pistol in his mouth and shattered his brain with a single bullet. His mistress, Eva Braun, whom he had married only hours before, chose to kill herself with poison. History records that their bodies were taken up to a yard behind the Chancellery and burnt.

Tasman, Ismail and some of the Commission workers were completing a lengthy work stint and were at Plugge's Plateau cemetery, the smallest on the Peninsula, when John Smith galloped up on a horse.

'I didn't know you could ride, John,' Tasman called out as Smith dismounted.

'It's over! It's bloody over, Tasman,' Smith shouted.

Clearly Smith was *very* excited – Tasman couldn't recall him ever using his first name before. 'What's over?' he asked.

'The bloody war, Tasman! The war in Europe is over.'

Tasman sat down quietly. It seemed right that he should hear the news at a place where the fallen of another war lay at peace. He tried to smile, but instead he found himself weeping.

The price of freedom had been high during the battle for Europe. But in the Pacific the price was still being paid.

Four weeks after the German surrender early in May 1945, Smith received a signal from British Intelligence. It was for Millington. He was to proceed without delay to dispose of the vessel and weaponry in his charge. London wanted no embarrassing incidents that might annoy its new ally Turkey, which had declared war on Germany when the conflict was almost over.

Tasman went to Suvla alone, having asked Ismail and Smith to meet him at sea the following morning in the old Commission launch, *Mary*. The rendezvous was to be five kilometres off Anzac Cove, one of the most poignant sites on the Peninsula.

At Suvla Tasman declined the Russian workers' offer of hospitality and went straight down to the MTB. Sitting on the afterdeck in the darkness he thought about the things he and his friends had achieved on this boat. He had no wish for the morning to come, knowing that in scuttling the MTB he would be drowning a part of his life.

But the morning did come. Waiting off Anzac Cove, Tasman watched as the *Mary* drew alongside. He greeted the others, then went below to the engine room and opened the bilge seacocks. When he crossed to the launch, Ismail steered away. The three men looked on silently as the MTB went down by the stern, its battered armour-plating creating a final turbulence in the water.

Late in June, Smith was given orders to report to the British mission in Istanbul for a debriefing, after which he was to return to England. Tasman had business in Istanbul as well and Ismail was more than anxious to get away from his mother-in-law for a day or two, so they went with Smith. Istanbul had become a Mecca for the displaced and, in the short time since the war ended in Europe, it had also become home to many Germanic-looking men who sat alone sipping tea in cafés and wearing suits they clearly hadn't purchased in Turkey.

Neither Tasman nor Ismail ever really learnt how Smith had come to know the man who knocked on the door of his hotel room late on the second day, a man he quickly ushered inside.

'I know this chap,' Smith said to them after a few words in German with the visitor. 'He's been working in the Resistance and has some interesting news. I think we should hear him out.'

The middle-aged German explained through Smith that there was a notorious war criminal in Istanbul. He was travelling on a Vatican passport under the auspices of the Nazis' Operation Bernhard, which offered escape routes financed by the SS. Furthermore, the informant said, he knew why the man was in Turkey. He'd come to collect looted gold and diamonds the SS had been sending to Istanbul for years. He travelled freely in the guise of a Catholic priest. And he was no ordinary SS officer. His real name was Heinrich Müller – 'Gestapo Müller' as tens of thousands of his victims had known him. The head of the SS.

Smith probed the information in depth before telling Tasman and Ismail that he was certain it was correct. Heinrich Müller had destroyed every photograph of himself that he could locate, months ago. He'd known the end was near and had made sure there'd be few who could identify him, let alone follow him. But the informant had seen him in Berlin and was positive.

Tasman, Smith and Ismail went that evening to the hotel where the man in the clothes of a priest was staying. Ismail remained outside and kept watch. Tasman wanted proof, more than the informant could provide, that the man was in fact Müller. On some pretext, Smith asked at the reception desk for his room number, then he and Tasman went quickly upstairs and knocked on the door. It was opened by a man, dressed in a priest's cassock, who asked in German what they wanted. Smith pushed the man backward through the doorway, causing him to stagger and fall. As soon as they were inside the room Tasman closed the door.

Smith talked with the priest, who was still on the floor. The conversation went on for several minutes until Smith reached down and pulled the man up. Smith then turned and said a few words to Tasman in German. The Australian nodded but remained silent. The priest brushed himself down and moved toward a small suitcase on the side-table. He opened the case and as he did so Tasman produced a .38 revolver and shot him several times.

Smith and Tasman raced downstairs, brushing past an alarmed desk clerk in the lobby. As they sat down with Ismail in a café a few streets away, Smith asked: 'How did you know it was Müller?'

Tasman smiled. 'You spoke to me in German. And you know I don't speak German.'

In the morning, after breakfast and a strangely awkward farewell, Smith went off to the British mission and Tasman and Ismail caught the ferry back to Chanak.

EPILOGUE

I met Pasha Ismail many years afterwards on another ferry, the one that runs through the Ionian Sea between Italy and Greece. I was on my way to Athens, as he was. Ismail offered me one of his Turkish cigarettes and we got talking. And so I came to know something of Tasman Millington.

At Patrai, where the ferry docked, we each took the coach to Athens, and Ismail went on with his story. As we stepped down into the warm night air of the city, I asked: 'Where are you staying, Ismail?'

The decision was made for both of us when we saw that we were standing outside a hotel and that our luggage was already being carried in by a porter. 'Perhaps we will be staying here, my friend,'

Ismail laughed. 'Let's hope they have good plumbing.'

'Why wouldn't they?' I asked.

'Because in the war, when the Germans eventually left Athens, they destroyed all the city's building plans – as a parting gesture.'

I stood at the window of my room, looking at the Acropolis surmounted by the beauty of the Parthenon. Illuminated by floodlights, it was one of those rare things beyond any price.

At breakfast Ismail asked if I'd been to Athens before.

'No, I haven't,' I said.

'Then I will show it to you today, if you wish. And I will tell you more about Millington.'

Old Athens is a city of marble. As we walked, we came to the Tomb of the Unknown Soldier and watched Greek troops in traditional uniform changing guard. From there we entered the Plaka, the central market area lined with countless shops selling goods and artefacts at a reasonable price if you're prepared to haggle. Beyond the Plaka lies the ancient Agora in the shadow of the Acropolis. But Ismail was feeling his years and wanted to sit down at a café.

'I will tell you this, my friend,' he said when the coffee came. 'If Millington was here, he would not tell you everything I have. Some things were too sacred, too emotional. He was always humbled by being the keeper of a timeless legend, the Anzac legend.'

For a long time Ismail was silent. Finally he said: 'Millington would have died a thousand deaths for every single man who lies on Gallipoli. Every grain of sand and every piece of soil was sacred to him. He devoted his soul to it for forty-two years.'

Ismail called to the waiter and ordered ouzo. 'Number twelve, if you've got it. It will ease the pain in my old legs.'

'After the war,' I said, 'what happened to the Italian – and all the others?'

'Ah, Gino, the "spy master". He went back to Italy. For him the war was *really* over!' Ismail laughed. 'This ouzo is making me feel much better.'

'And the others?'

The old Turk concentrated. 'One of the Australians visited Millington in the late 'fifties – not long after Mrs Millington died in 1956. Yuri became the captain of a fishing trawler on the Black Sea. He wrote to Millington over the years and I heard later that he drowned in a storm. The other Russians finally went home to start looking for their families. And the Greek major, Drakopoulos. Yes – he came to see Millington after the war. He lived here in Athens and he died in 1977.'

I poured another ouzo into our glasses. 'And John Smith? What happened to him?'

'Ah, yes, Smith. He came back often. But for some reason known only to the great Allah, he lived in a village in the west country of Wales. I have not seen him for many years now.'

I laughed. 'And you, Ismail, what about you?'

He waved the question aside. 'You do not really wish to hear of me, I am of little importance. However, I no longer live in Chanak – my son took me to live with him and his family in Istanbul. They say I am too old, though it doesn't stop me from travelling once every year. But I sometimes regret that I have never gone to Australia.'

'Maybe you still will,' I said.

'Maybe, but there's really no need,' Ismail replied. 'I have seen it many, many times through Millington's eyes ... and from four decades of listening to his yarns!'

Pasha Ismail and I parted company at Athens International Airport. 'You must visit me in Istanbul one day,' he said. 'And if you don't, I will see you after the sun rises on the world for the last time. But there is one other thing. When you tell people about

Millington and all the things I have told you, say that he was taught to be a soldier but learned the art of peace. And tell them that he was my friend – one who became my brother.'

On Anzac Day in 1948 a group of delegates attended a luncheon in Chanak, as the guests of the Turkish Army, on their way to the unveiling of a new war memorial at Tobruk in North Africa. They had paid a visit to Gallipoli. The lunch was informal and the conversation light and jovial. Tasman and Ismail had been invited and were standing together talking after the meal. Seeing Tasman there, General Sir Leslie Morshead, the famed commander of the 9th Australian Division, excused himself from the table and came over with a drink in his hand.

'Outstanding,' the general said, 'all the work you've done here with the War Graves Commission. A real credit to you, Millington!'

Tasman thanked him and then said: 'Sir, I'd like you to meet Pasha Ismail.'

General Morshead put out his hand. 'Nice to meet you,' he said, and turned to Tasman. 'One of your workers?' Tasman didn't answer. 'You're a lucky man, Millington,' the general went on. 'Such a peaceful place. And to think that only a few years ago you were surrounded by that damned war! You don't know how lucky you were to be out of it.'

Tasman glanced at Ismail. Both of them began to shake. Tears came to their eyes as they erupted in laughter. Tasman put a hand on Ismail's shoulder for support. The general stood there thoroughly dismayed and Millington's wife, sitting at the table, looked at them as if they'd gone utterly mad.

In the cold pre-dawn light of 25 April 1964, an old Turk weaved his way through the cypress trees and wild thyme, towards the cliffs high above Anzac Cove. The closer he came to the craggy clifftops, the more vivid his memories became of another morning, long ago, when he was a younger man and there for a very different reason. This morning, though, Ismail carried no weapon to repel an invader. Instead he carried in his cold, leathery hand a small and simple cardboard box containing the ashes of an old enemy who had come to be his good friend, Tasman Millington.

Standing alone upon the high ground above the beach, as the first rays of dawn lit the sky, Ismail cast the dust over the Aegean Sea. It lingered just for a moment in the soft seabreeze, then was gone.

Millington's mission was over.

They shall grow not old,
As we that are left grow old:
Age shall not weary them,
Nor the years condemn.
At the going down of the sun
And in the morning
We will remember them.

Lest we forget.

ACKNOWLEDGMENTS

I would like to thank the following for their assistance.

The Commonwealth War Graves Commission (Britain), in particular Peter Francis, John Worledge and Maria Cannon; David Saunders of the Gallipoli Association; Imperial War Museum, London; Office of SOE; Rachel Wells MVO, Central Chancery of the Orders of Knighthood, St James Palace; London *Times* Archives; Royal Navy; Royal Air Force; RSL of Australia; RSA of New Zealand; Australian Army, in particular the Intelligence Corps, Signals Corps and Central Army Records Office; National Archives of Australia; National Library of Australia; Australian War Memorial; Kostas Paterakis, whose knowledge of the battle for Crete remains ever clear; George Farran of Hamilton, New Zealand, the son of a New Zealand soldier who escaped Crete on Millington's MTB, and who thought it was time his father's private war in the Aegean was told to the world; the Reverend of St Georges Church, Battery Point, Hobart; the people of Chanak, Turkey; Government Records Office, Istanbul; French Embassy, Ankara; Greek Embassy, Canberra.

I also owe a special debt to my editorial mentor, John Ferguson, a former publisher at HarperCollins.

John Samuels was born in Sydney, and is a former photojournalist turned full-time non-fiction writer. He has a wide background of writing investigative articles for newspapers and magazines, but his main interest is uncovering unknown stories of Australian military heroes. He has also published a number of short stories and poems, including 'The Light Horsemen' and 'Known Unto God'. John Samuels lives on Queensland's Gold Coast.

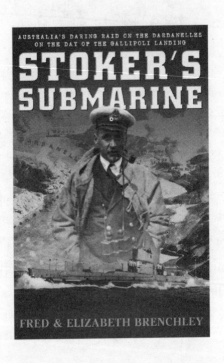

AUSTRALIA'S DARING RAID ON THE DARDANELLES
ON THE DAY OF THE GALLIPOLI LANDING

STOKER'S SUBMARINE

FRED & ELIZABETH BRENCHLEY

Stoker's Submarine

FRED AND ELIZABETH BRENCHLEY

The untold story of Australia's AE2 submarine and its mission impossible

On 25 April 1915, the day the Anzacs landed at Gallipoli, Lt Commander Dacre Stoker set out as captain of the Australian submarine *AE2* on a mission to navigate the Dardanelles Strait. That Stoker managed to find a way through the narrow Dardanelles against unknown currents, mines and withering enemy fire has been described as 'the finest feat in submarine history', yet his achievement meant as much in emotional terms for the boost it gave the morale of the embattled Allied troops. *Stoker's Submarine* tells the story of a remarkable naval achievement, which until now has been little celebrated.

'. . . *a cracking good story. The Brenchleys . . . make the very most of AE2's short but spectacular wartime career and its subsequent history.*' Weekend Australian

'*Fred and Elizabeth have done us all a literary and patriotic favour in recounting the story of Stoker, his crew and the AE2.*' Kim Beazley

073226703X